Servicing Electronic Systems Volume 2, Part 3

Control System Technology

**A Textbook for the
City and Guilds of London Institute Course No. 224
(as revised 1990)
and for
The Technician Education Council Level II Course in Electronics**

by
Ian R. Sinclair
B.Sc.
*Formerly Lecturer in Physics & Electronics
Braintree (Essex) College of Further Education*

and

Geoffrey E. Lewis
B.A., M.Sc., M.R.T.S., M.I.E.E.I.E.
*Formerly Senior Lecturer in Radio, Television and Electronics,
Canterbury College of Technology*

Avebury Technical

Avebury Technical,
Ashgate Publishing Limited,
Gower House,
Croft Road,
Aldershot,
Hants GU11 3HR,
England

Ashgate Publishing Company,
Old Post Road,
Brookfield,
Vermont 05036,
USA

A CIP catalogue record for this book is available from the British Library and the US Library of Congress

ISBN 1 85628 811 0

Typeset in 10 point Times by Poole Typesetting (Wessex) Ltd, Bournemouth, Printed and bound in Great Britain by Dotesios Ltd, Trowbridge, Wiltshire.

Contents

Preface

As the end of the century approaches, the technology of electronics that was born in the twentieth century is by now the dominant technology in all aspects of our lives. The very nature of electronics has changed enormously in our lifetimes, from its beginnings in radio to its involvement in control of everything from food mixers to car engine performance, from games to industrial empires.

All of this makes the task of servicing electronics equipment more specialized, more demanding and more important. Servicing personnel play a very important part in maintaining the correct operation of a system. They not only need to develop a high level of diagnostic skills but they also need to be able to communicate their findings to others so that the reliability and testability of a system can be improved. This then may also demand the further skills required to modify an in-service system. In particular, the training of anyone who will specialize in servicing must be geared to the speed and nature of the changes that are continually taking place. This involves a sound knowledge of electronic principles and the development of diagnostic skills, neither of which is likely to be superseded by any changes of technology. Another important factor is that with the increasing harmonization of technical standards in Europe, it is likely that knowledge of technical terms in several European languages will become an essential part of the training for servicing work. For that reason, a polyglot glossary of technical terms has been included in the appendices.

This series of books is designed primarily to cover the most recent requirements of the City & Guilds of London Course No. 224 in Electronics Servicing, and also to provide coverage of the equivalent BTEC course. The approach is systems-based, viewing each electronic component or assembly as a device with known inputs and outputs. In this way, changes in technology do not require changes in the methods and principles of servicing, only to the everyday practical aspects which are continually changing in any case.

We have also taken every opportunity to look beyond the confines of the present syllabuses to the likely requirements of the future, and particularly to the impact of a single European market on both electronics and training. The books will invariably be amended in line with changes in the syllabuses and in the development of electronics, but the aim will be at all times to concentrate on the fundamentals of diagnosis and repair of whatever electronics equipment will require servicing in years to come.

A guide book has been prepared which contains useful course hints together with comments on the questions included in the main text. This booklet, which may be freely photocopied, is available free of charge to lecturers and instructors from:

Customer Services,
Avebury Technical,
Gower Publishing Co. Ltd,
Gower House,
Croft Road,
Aldershot,
Hampshire GU11 3HR.

Acknowledgements

The authors gratefully acknowledge the permission of the City & Guilds of London Institute and the Electronics Examination Board to reproduce extracts and circuit diagrams from Course 224, Electronics Servicing (new scheme) syllabus and regulations. Abridged versions of these have been included in the appendices and used as a cross-reference to the contents of the various chapters. For precise details of the scheme, the reader is referred to the full Part II syllabuses available from the City & Guilds of London Institute, 76 Portland Place, London W1N 4AA, and the Electronics Examination Board, Savoy Hill House, Savoy Hill, London WC2R 0BS.

Further, grateful thanks are extended to: Feedback Instruments Ltd, Park Road, Crowborough, East Sussex TN6 2QR; LJ Technical Systems Ltd, Francis Way, Bowthorpe Industrial Estate, Norwich NR5 9JA; and TQ International Ltd, Bonsall Street, Long Eaton, Nottingham NG10 2AN. All are providers of educational and training equipment designed to simulate real control systems under actual working and fault conditions. It is from the training manuals associated with these systems that many of the exercises and test questions have been developed.

In particular, the authors would like formally to recognize the valuable assistance provided by Gerry Tulett of Feedback Instruments Ltd, Alan Gray, Head of Department, Havering College, Keith Webster of LJ Technical Systems Ltd, John Lewis, TQ International Ltd, and Morten Moller of Control Transducers Ltd.

Introduction

This book covers the option Control Systems Technology of the City & Guilds of London Institute, Course 224, Electronics Servicing at the Part II level. It thus complements Volume 2 Part 1 of this series, *Basic Principles and Circuits (Core Studies)*. Unlike the majority of texts dedicated to control system technology, this book deals with the topic in a practical and non-mathematical way. Indeed, many of the assessment objectives can be achieved by following exercises based on system training simulators. With regard to the suggested practical activities, the importance of *safe working practice* cannot be too strongly stressed. The general objectives of this part of the course are to ensure that the student can:

- set up, test and locate faults in basic control systems and subsystems;
- understand the principles and applications of electronic control systems in an industrial situation;
- interpret manufacturers' data and select equivalent components;
- read and interpret circuit and layout diagrams;
- select suitable test instruments for a particular situation;
- diagnose single component faults and identify their effects.

1   Basic control systems

Summary

Open- and closed-loop systems. Definition of terminology. Elements of control systems. Analogue control. Digital control. Basic controllers. (Syllabus section 7.1)

Introduction to system control

Circuits and components that behave well in domestic (radio, audio, TV) equipment are often unsuitable for use in industrial and telecommunications applications. The operating conditions under which much industrial electronic equipment has to work are stringent. Special difficulties encountered include the following:

1 *Greater temperature ranges.* In particular, the temperature of the surrounding air (the *ambient temperature*) cannot safely be assumed never to rise above a maximum of 30 °C, as is the case with most domestic equipment.
2 *Interference pulses.* Industrial electronic equipment is often subject to heavy pulse interference, both radiated and received through the a.c. supply lines.
3 *Mains voltage fluctuations.* The value of the mains a.c. voltage supply can be expected to alter sharply whenever large electric motors are switched on and off.
4 *Fail-safe operation.* Safey conditions often demand that any electronic failure must result in machinery *stopping* — never continuing to run on.

1

5   *The need for greater reliability*. The failure of a TV receiver is an incon-
venience. The failure of a large electronically controlled machine tool could
cause disaster.

To meet these demanding conditions, extensive use is made of integrated circuits (ICs) for the following reasons:

1   A high degree of integration produces fewer external leads, soldered joints
and interconnections able to develop *dry joints*.
2   A greatly reduced physical size is possible, particularly if *surface-mount
technology* (SMT) is employed.
3   Faster circuits that operate at higher frequencies are possible because of
shorter signal path lengths with lower self-capacitance.
4   IC fabrication gives better control over the spread or variation of device
parameters.
5   Final system design and performance can be more closely controlled.

In higher-power applications, dedicated *thick-film devices* may be employed.
These are formed by depositing a layer of metal on an insulator base of either
glass, sapphire or vitreous enamel. ICs and other chip-type components are then
attached in a similar way to printed circuit boards. (By comparison, normal ICs
are described as *thin-film devices*.) ICs are used in both analogue and digital
controllers and may be fabricated in either bipolar or CMOS technology. It is
therefore necessary to recognize the different properties, characteristics and
robustness of each under normal and fault conditions.

Since most controllers will be electronic devices operating in an industrial
environment, in the interests of safety it is important to recognize that two earth
concepts might be encountered. The main *protective earth* (PE) is provided on
the mains power supply and the *functional earth* (FE) is provided within the
equipment. PE is provided to protect life and equipment; FE provides a point
for zero volts reference, a common point for interference suppression, and a
signal path return within the controlled system. Under no circumstances should
the two be separated under normal working conditions.

A *system* is defined as an assembly of components, interconnected in an
organized manner to perform some particular function. It therefore has *inputs*
upon which to perform some specific task to produce a particular *goal* or
output. By comparison, a *servo mechanism* is a system designed to provide
mechanical positioning, sometimes in association with a human physical input.

Open- and closed-loop systems

As indicated in Figure 1.1(a), the process is controlled via a controlling device
and a *reference input* or *set point* value. Such a system does not and cannot

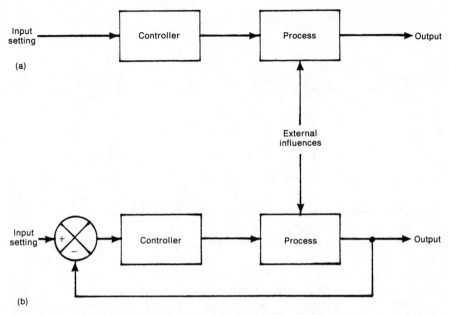

Figure 1.1   (a) Open-loop system; (b) closed-loop system

counteract the effects of external influences. In real life, such systems have little value and require extensive human monitoring. For example, assume some process requires a continual but variable supply of water. This might be provided via a reservoir tank that is refilled from a continuous supply using a valve as the controlling element. A human operator might then set this valve so that, over a period of time, the average output needs are met by the average input, without the tank drying out or overflowing. However, this does not take into consideration other external influences. The tank might develop a leak or the mains supply pressure might change. In either case, a disaster could arise. These problems could be avoided by adding a float-controlled inlet valve, where the float level automatically adjusted the level of water to meet the needs of the process. The addition of automatic monitor and control converts the system into a *closed-loop* one by the addition of *negative feedback*. The distinction between open-loop and closed-loop systems is shown in Figure 1.1(a) and (b), where the system outputs represent the process-controlled variable quantity, in this case the water level.

Definition of terminology

The principal elements of a control system are depicted in Figure 1.2 where a part of the output signal is applied together with a reference value to a compara-tor or error detector. The difference between these two values is then used to

3

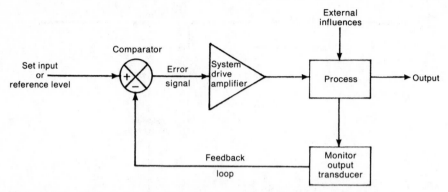

Figure 1.2   Notional control system used to define terminology

drive the system to maintain a constant output condition by driving the error signal towards zero. Since any output-monitoring device is likely only to produce very low-amplitude signals (either voltage or current), amplification will be necessary to generate sufficient power to drive the controller stage. Any disturbing external influence on the system is then automatically corrected through negative feedback. Such an automatic control system can be subdivided into four main stages:

1   Measure the output.
2   Provide a reference input.
3   Generate an error signal.
4   Control the process.

Although control of the system may be via electrical/electronic means, the output function may vary widely from, say, packaging control on a production line to environmental control of an office block.

Reference or set point input   This is the user input level that represents the desired value of the process variable being controlled.

Output   This represents the process variable quantity that is to be controlled.

Comparator   This is the element that generates the *error signal*.

Error signal   This is the difference between the set point or reference level and the value derived by monitoring the output. It is sometimes referred to as the system *deviation*.

Controller   This is the system element that is driven by the error signal which in turn drives the process in an attempt to minimize the error signal.

4

Proportional control   This is exerted by any system in which the output from the controller is directly proportional to its input error signal.

On-off control   This is a system in which the controller has only two positions, either on or off. Control is thus exerted in a continuous oscillatory manner about some process average. It is sometimes described as *bang–bang* control.

Accuracy   This is the precision with which a system returns to its reference state following some external disturbance.

Offset   Theoretically the error signal should be driven to zero after some disturbance. However, in any practical system, this will not quite be achieved. The difference between the reference value and the final error value is thus described as the *offset*.

Dead band   This is the range of reference or command values for which the system does not respond. This tends to be greater for electromechanical systems because static friction (*stiction*) is higher than rolling friction. To counteract this effect, a low amplitude a.c. signal (dither) may be added to the d.c. error signal to *unstick* the mechanism.

Proportional band   The proportional band of control is the total range over which the controller is capable of exerting a control over a given system. For example, a temperature controller in a particular system may be capable of operating over a range from 20 °C to 100 °C, giving a proportional band of control of 80 °C. Owing to the *proportional gain* of this system, the controller may only operate proportionally over a much narrower range, such as ± 15°. The system's *proportional band* would then be stated as 30/80 = 0.375 or 37.5%. Generally, the product of proportional band and proportional gain for a given system tends, within limits, to be constant. A narrow proportional band with its attendant high proportional gain yields a small offset.

Stability   The combination of a high-speed response to a disturbance and a small offset can lead to instability. When such a system reacts suddenly to a change, it generates a large error signal that overcorrects. This then produces a further overcorrection in the opposite sense and the system oscillates. During this period, the system is effectively out of control, and unless the oscillation decays, the system will self-destruct. Stability is thus closely related to *damping*.

Damping   This is electrically equivalent to shunting a resonant circuit with a resistance or mechanically loading a *springy* system with a shock-absorber. When a high-gain system experiences a sudden change, there is a tendency for

5

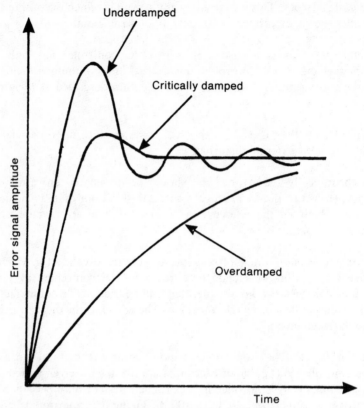

Figure 1.3   System damping response

the error signal to oscillate in the manner shown in Figure 1.3. By adding resistance to the control circuit, the response speed is slowed somewhat but the oscillations become controlled. *Critical damping* is defined as shown, with just one overshoot before the system settles once again to its equilibrium state. Overdamping removes any overshoot but produces a relatively slow response to a change.

Transport lag (transfer lag)   For sudden disturbances the controller makes a partial immediate response but the system takes a period of time (lag) to settle down to a new equilibrium. Electrically this is equivalent to the low-pass filtering of a square-wave pulse.

Defining a 'good' system

High proportional gain provides a narrow proportional band to give close control over system variability. Too high a gain can lead to an unstable system.

Low proportional gain provides a slow response to any change and a wide range of command levels, but increases the dead band and the offset. A 'good' system is thus one that:

1   is stable and responds quickly to any external disturbance;
2   reduces the error signal practically to zero (low offset), to give close control of the process variable.

Elements of control systems

Transducer or sensor

A transducer is a device that converts energy from one form to another. In this case, the required final energy form is electrical. The difference between transducers and sensors is very slight. A sensor is used to detect and measure some physical quantity and therefore must act in the same way as a transducer. However, the transducer is normally required to have a good energy-conversion factor, whereas a sensor is needed to have a linear response to changes in the parameter being measured. The *responsivity* or sensitivity of a transducer is measured by the ratio

$$\frac{\text{Electrical output signal level}}{\text{Input quantity level}}$$

Both signals are usually measured in watts.

Because these devices have to work in noisy situations, the *detectivity* of a transducer is defined by the ratio

$$\frac{\text{Signal-to-noise ratio of the output signal}}{\text{Amplitude of the input quantity}}$$

Essentially, the function of the transducer is to provide an electrical signal that represents the variable property of the system that is to be controlled. In most cases, this signal will be very small, so that transducers should be very sensitive and preferably linear. For this reason, *bridge amplifiers* often form part of this element. It will be recalled that the Wheatstone bridge shown in Figure 1.4(a) is balanced when the products of the opposite resistive arms are equal, i.e. when $R_1R_4 = R_2R_3$. This condition causes the voltage V_b to be equal to zero. One resistance in the bridge, supposed in this case to be R_3, will act as the sensor and be exposed in a suitable manner to the changing condition being monitored. As the bridge unbalances, V_b will swing either positively or negatively depending upon the exact effect of the system variability on the sensor device (R_3). In the interests of bridge stability, R_4 is often replaced by a second identical sensor that

7

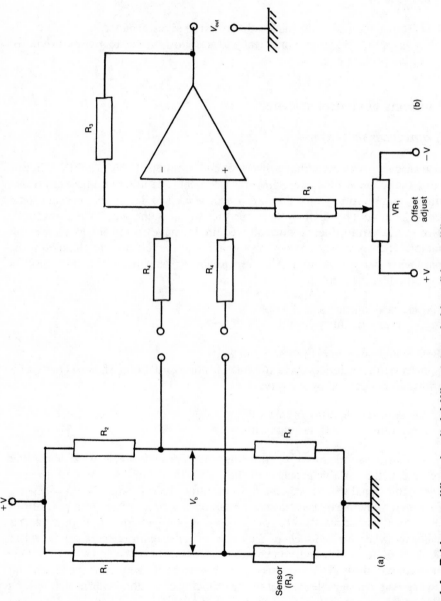

Figure 1.4 Bridge amplifier circuit: (a) Wheatstone bridge; (b) amplifier

8

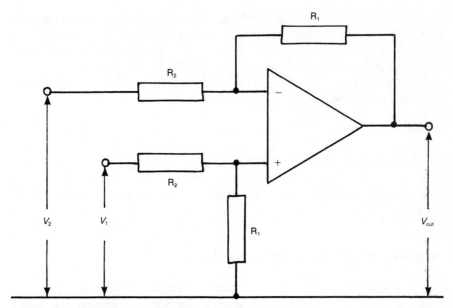

Figure 1.5 Comparator circuit

is shielded from the system changes. Any drift in bridge component values due to time and ambient temperature will then be self-cancelling.

A further advantage of the bridge circuit is its ability to be a.c.-energized. The unbalanced signal is then a.c. and this is easily amplified for transmission over lines to a remote-controller circuit. The associated amplifier, shown in Figure 1.4(b), is the differential amplifier that is effectively driven in a push–pull mode. This provides a high gain with good rejection of common-mode interference signals. Also shown in Figure 1.4(b) is an alternative method of nulling out the amplifier's *input offset voltage*. Since the gain of this amplifier is proportional to the resistance ratio R_3/R_4, the output voltage V_{out} is proportional to the unbalance voltage from the bridge circuit.

Comparator

It will be recalled that the gain of an operational amplifier (opamp) depends upon the ratio of the programming resistors R_1 and R_2 of Figure 1.5. For the inverting input $(-)$ the gain is given by $-R_1/R_2$ and for the non-inverting input $(+)$ by $1+R_1/R_2$. If all the resistors are of equal value, then if V_2 is held at zero volts, the output voltage V_{out} will follow the polarity of V_1. Because $R_1=R_2$ the actual input to $(+)$ will be $V_1/2$. Since the gain at this input is 2, $V_{out} = +V_1$. If V_1 is now held at zero volts as V_2 is varied, the signal inversion and unity gain will produce $V_{out} = -V_2$. Since the amplifier is operating in a linear mode, these two results can be superimposed to give $V_{out} = V_1 - V_2$, showing that it

9

produces an output that is proportional to the difference between the two inputs. Thus if V_1 is the reference or set point level and V_2 is the measured signal from the system output, the circuit behaves as an error detector or comparator. If the two resistors R_1 are given a value of GR_1 (R_2 values unchanged), the amplifier will have a gain of G so that $V_{out} = -G(V_2 - V_1)$, a feature that is particularly valuable in the bridge amplifier circuit.

Controller

This component could be an electrical, mechanical, pneumatic or hydraulic device, electrically driven to control the system variable. In all except the very simple and almost trivial cases, it will be driven from the error signal via voltage and power amplifiers.

Analogue temperature control system

The basic system for maintaining a stable temperature in an electric oven is shown in Figure 1.6. The potentiometer R_1 provides a positive voltage proportional to its setting to be used as the reference level. This is therefore described as the set-temperature control.

At start-up, the oven temperature will be low, as will be the voltage developed by the sensor. The inputs to the comparator thus have a large and positive difference, so that the output is also high and positive. This causes the heater drive amplifier to deliver a high current to the oven heater element. As the temperature rises, so does the voltage developed by the sensor. The comparator differential input falls, reducing the drive current to the amplifier and thus the heater.

As the oven reaches the set temperature, the differential input to the comparator drops towards zero and the heater current cuts off. As the oven cools, the sensor output falls in proportion so that the differential input increases to cause more current to be delivered to the oven heater. Eventually the system stabilizes with the drive current oscillating between limits to maintain the temperature within an acceptable band. Raising or lowering the slider on R_1 will cause the oven temperature to stabilize at a higher or lower temperature.

Computer-controlled systems

The development of low-cost digital computers has led to their adoption as the controlling element in many systems. Because they can be reprogrammed, a given type of computer can be used in many different situations. It is this sort of flexibility that has led to their reduced costs. Figure 1.7 shows an example of

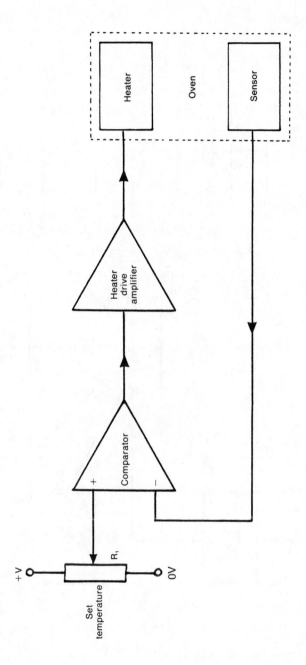

Figure 1.6 Analogue temperature control system

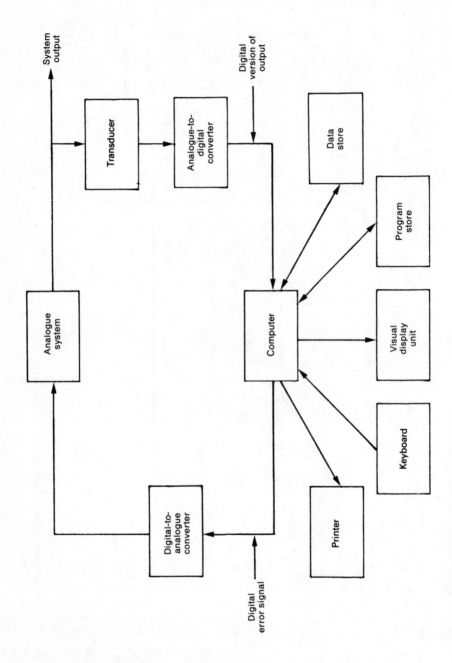

Figure 1.7   A computer-controlled system

12

such a system, whose functions might include that of automatic test equipment (ATE). In such cases, data about the product's test parameters have to be measured, recorded (logged) and then presented in such a way that quality control can operate. The system's output values are monitored by transducers that generate analogue signals. Although analogue computers are available, they are much less flexible than their digital counterparts and therefore tend to be used less often. The transducer's output is converted into a digital signal by the *analogue-to-digital* converter.

At this stage, the exact use of this data signal depends upon the computer's function within the system. If it is simply 'test and measure' then the data will be stored for future use and/or printed out on paper. Warning signals may also be displayed on the visual display unit (VDU) if the measurements are drifting out of specification. If necessary, the test program and/or the specification can be modified from the keyboard. In a control system, the data will be compared with predetermined values held in the computer's memory so that a digital version of an 'error signal' can be generated. After conversion back into analogue form in the digital-to-analogue converter this signal is applied to the system input as a correcting influence.

Analogue-to-digital conversion

The principle of analogue-to-digital (A/D) conversion is shown in Figure 1.8(a). The analogue signal amplitude is sampled at regular intervals of time under the control of the sampler clock. These amplitudes are then converted into a binary code representing their level, as shown in Figure 1.8(b).

Digital-to-analogue conversion

The binary coded values are input to the converter (shown in Figure 1.9(a)) to restore the analogue waveform. However, the wave now contains a strong unwanted signal component at the sampling frequency and this is removed by the low-pass filter.

Digital temperature control system

The oven, heater, driver amplifier and sensor function in the analogue mode, but the error signal, reference input and control action are handled by the digital controller in the manner indicated in Figure 1.10. The output signal provided by the sensor is transformed into a binary digital bit stream by the A/D converter. This is passed to the computer where it is compared with the previous user input reference value, to generate a digital version of the error signal. When this signal is converted into analogue form by the D/A converter it

13

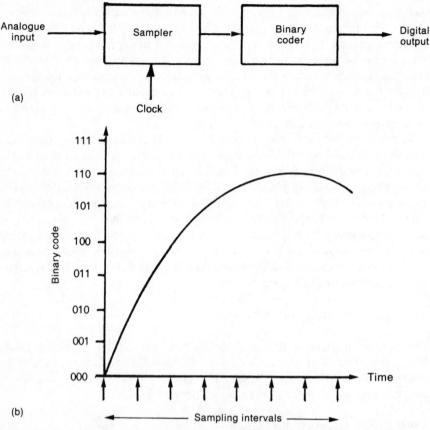

Figure 1.8 (a) Principle of analogue-to-digital conversion; (b) amplitude sampling

can be used to control the heater current in the normal way. Thus as far as the heater system is involved, there is practically no difference between this and the analogue control technique. The action and architecture of the computer and microprocessor were extensively covered in Volume 2 Part 1 of this series, but the following provides an explanation of the device as applied specifically to control systems.

For the computer to be connected as part of a control system, it must be able to interact with a wide range of external devices known as *peripherals*. It is unusual to be able to couple any peripheral directly to the computer because of various differences. A device known as an *interface* is used to overcome the incompatibility problems, which may include:

1 *Electrical*. Different voltage, current or impedance levels may exist.
2 *Timing*. The computer and peripherals may work at different data rates.

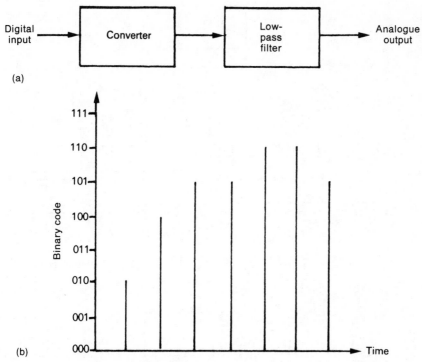

(a)

(b)

Figure 1.9   (a) Principle of digital-to-analogue conversion; (b) plot of digital values from Figure 1.8(b)

3   *Codes.* The computer often functions on 8-bit bytes. The code pattern length for the peripheral may be different and this involves a change in the number of communicating data lines.

In general, interfaces are usually unique to particular applications, but a number of *universal chips* are available to simplify the problem. These are variously known as *peripheral interface adaptors* (PIA) or *parallel input/output* (PIO) devices. Most of these chips are capable of controlling two input/output (I/O) ports, each eight lines wide with each line capable of being programmed to act as an input or output. Figure 1.10 indicates the central role of communications performed by the I/O device.

The main highways of communications between the various sections are known as *buses*. These commonly consist of parallel conducting paths of either 8 or 16 lines. The address bus is used to identify the location of each item of information as it is required and this is then transferred over the data bus. These operations are carried out under the control of signals placed on the control bus. Addresses are all generated by the microprocessor so that this bus is described as being *unidirectional*. By comparison, the data bus is *bidirectional*.

15

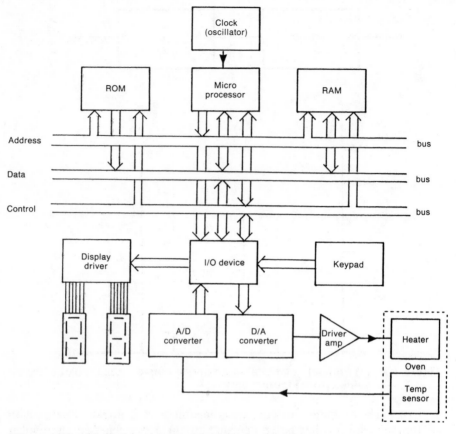

Figure 1.10   Digitally controlled temperature system

The strictly controlled timing of the data manipulation is managed by a *clock* or crystal-controller oscillator. As this often runs at a frequency of 1 MHz in many system controllers, accurate timing pulses are generated every 1 μs.

In addition to the program that controls the way the system operates, the memory has to hold or store data items that are waiting to be processed. This requires two types of memory device. One, which retains its information even when the power is switched off, is known as *read-only memory* (ROM) and carries the processor operating instructions. The other, which has to be capable of being *written to* or *read from* in an almost random manner, is described as *random-access memory* (RAM). Because of its retentive memory, ROM is described as being *non-volatile* while RAM, which loses its data when the power is switched off, is said to be *volatile*.

As well as providing the user with a means of inputting locally required reference points, the keypad or keyboard gives the controller a wide degree of

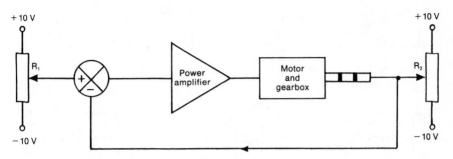

Figure 1.11   Position control system

flexibility. By this means, the computer can be reprogrammed to operate in a wide range of different control systems.

In this particular application, a *seven-segment display* is used to provide a visual indication of the oven temperature.

Three-term controllers

Practical proportional (P) control systems must always operate with some offset value. This means that the error signal does not fall to absolute zero and so the design problem is to make this an acceptably low value. This is equivalent to hysteresis in an electrical sense and backlash in a mechanical system. Proportional controllers are therefore best used where the load conditions change only slowly and the relative drift from the reference point is small.

The problem can be resolved by adding a parallel *time integral* (I) function to produce a P + I-controlled system. The control action then operates as follows. The proportion term positions the controller with a small offset. The remaining error is then time-integrated so that this small value accumulates to drive the controller to a position that gives a zero error. Integrating a zero value produces a zero output, so that the system now becomes accurately stabilized. In systems where a control time lag exists or rapid load changes can occur, P + I control may not be completely effective. By adding a third *derivative* (D) function in parallel, (P + I + D) in the form of a differentiator circuit, provision is made to correct any fast-changing errors. The comparator circuit then becomes three opamps in parallel, whose outputs are summed in a fourth amplifier to provide the correcting drive signal.

Position control system

This type of system, depicted in Figure 1.11, is often used to control the rotational or linear position of some indicating or mechanical device. The

17

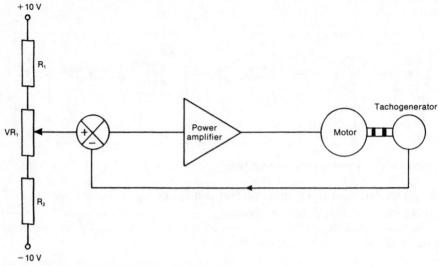

Figure 1.12   Speed control system

potentiometer R_1 provides a d.c. voltage dependent upon its setting to give the reference or set point value. This is input to the comparator along with a d.c. signal derived from the system output. The error signal generated from this stage is used to drive the power amplifier stages. These will normally be powered from a dual polarity supply so that the motor can be driven in forward or reverse modes. The potentiometer R_2 which is directly coupled to the motor-driven gear box acts as the *measure output* sensor to provide a d.c. voltage proportional to its slider position. This potentiometer may be of either the rotary or linear type depending upon the type of positioning required.

If R_1 is set to $+5$ V while R_2 is producing 0 V, the differential input to the comparator will be high and positive. This will cause the power amplifier to deliver a positive current to the motor so that it runs forward to drive R_2 to produce $+5$ V. The feedback voltage therefore rises during rotation so that the error voltage falls to zero at the same rate, when the motor will halt. If the reference voltage is now reduced, or made negative by adjustment of R_1, the amplifier will deliver a negative current to the motor so that it runs in reverse to take up a new position as the voltage across R_2 approaches that provided by R_1.

Speed control system

The potential divider network R_1, VR_1 and R_2 shown in Figure 1.12 provides a reference input voltage that acts as *set speed* control. This is input to the comparator along with a voltage derived from the system output *tachogenerator*. This is a device that generates a d.c. voltage proportional to its rotational

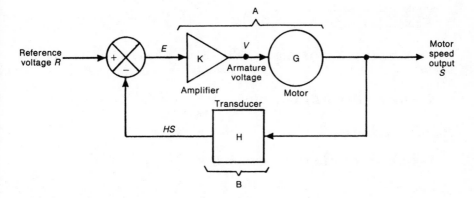

Figure 1.13   Speed control system dynamics

speed, and hence that of the motor, to which it is directly coupled. When the set speed and feedback voltages are practically equal, the comparator output (error signal) is zero. The power amplifier then delivers sufficient current to cause the motor to run at its designed speed. If it is required to increase the motor speed, VR_1 is adjusted to provide a more positive voltage. The comparator output then becomes positive to increase the drive to the power amplifier. This now delivers more current to the motor, causing it to stabilize quickly to the new speed setting.

If the load on the motor decreases, its speed will tend to rise, as will the output from the tachogenerator. Since the set speed level has not been changed, the increased feedback voltage will cause the comparator to produce a negative error signal. This reduces the power output from the drive amplifier and causes the motor speed to fall to match the new load demand. The reverse action occurs if the motor load increases. Resistors R_1 and R_2 are often included in the reference input circuit, to restrict the range of control action and to limit the current flowing through the set speed potentiometer.

Control system dynamics

The elements of a closed-loop speed-control system are shown in Figure 1.13. For a given input voltage V, the motor produces an output speed of S rpm. The directly coupled transducer produces an output voltage for feedback that is directly proportional to S, so that the output from block H (the feedback loop) is HS with units of V/rpm. If the reference level has a value of R volts, the comparator generates an error signal (E) of $R - HS$. The amplifier has gain K, so that $V = KE$ or $V = K(R - HS)$.

The parameter G for the motor is given by

$$\frac{\text{Stable output state}}{\text{Stable input state}}$$

so that $G = S/V$ or $S = GV$. Since $V = KE$, $S = GKE$ and substituting for $E = R - HS$,

$$S = GK(R - HS) = GKR - GKHS$$

Rearranging this gives

$$S + GKHS = GKR \text{ or } S(1 + GKH) = GKR$$

and

$$S/R = \frac{GK}{1 + GKH}$$

where S/R is described as the *closed-loop gain* or *transfer function* for the system. If the circuit is simplified by putting $A = GK$ and $B = H$, the equation becomes

$$S/R = \frac{A}{1 + AB}$$

which is the equation for the closed-loop gain of an amplifier with negative feedback.

System tuning

The aim of system tuning is to set the gain of the amplifier and the frequency response of any compensation network, so that the system quickly settles down to a stable state, following a step input disturbance. Of the many methods described in the literature, the *half amplitude* method provides a very useful starting point for system fine tuning. Here the error signal is monitored on an oscilloscope and the system presets are adjusted until the successive amplitudes of the overshoots and undershoots, as shown in the underdamped waveform of Figure 1.14, fall by more than a half, ie $a > 2b$.

Exercise 1.1

Construct the circuit shown in Figure 1.15(a) and (b) either on a circuit or a breadboard. (In some circumstances it may be convenient to omit the 10 kΩ load resistor.) With R_1 and R_2 set to mid-range, short pins 2 and 3 to the 0 V line. Using an electronic voltmeter to measure V_{out}, vary R_3 over its whole range

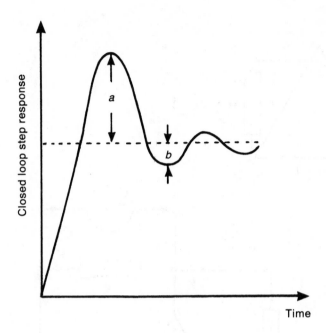

Figure 1.14   Half-amplitude tuning response

and record the effect of the opamp input offset voltage, then set V_{out} to zero. Replace the short circuits at pins 2 and 3 with voltmeters. Set pin 3 voltage to zero using R_2 and vary the voltage at pin 2 over the range ± 1 V recording the behaviour of V_{out}. Repeat this step for pin 2 at 0 V while varying R_1 over the same range. Does this circuit behave as a comparator? What would be the effect on a system control if R_3 was incorrectly set?

Exercise 1.2

Using either one of the EEB test boards, or one of the proprietary training systems wired for proportional control, open-circuit the feedback loop to the comparator stage. (Either a speed or position control system will produce the fastest results.) Adjust the input reference/command control and observe the effect on the output device. Now apply some external disturbance and note the effect that it has. This can be countered only by readjusting the system input setting, because the open-loop system has no way of generating a correcting influence. Now close the feedback loop and repeat the exercise. Within limits, the closed-loop system now has the ability to correct for the same external disturbing influences.

22

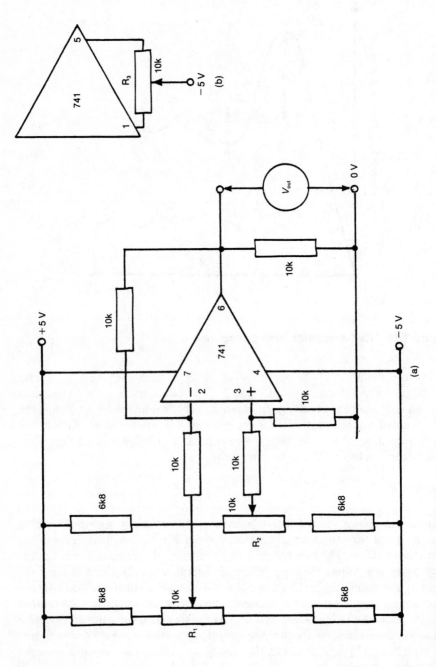

Figure 1.15 Circuit for Exercise 1.1

Exercise 1.3

Interconnect a proportional speed control system in the manner indicated in Figure 1.12, using a calibrated tachogenerator. Include an inverting opamp with variable gain control, between the comparator and the motor drive amplifier. Connect a multimeter switched to a suitable d.c. range to the motor drive amplifier input and call this V_{in}. Switch on and note that the reference level control varies the motor speed as indicated on a second d.c. voltmeter connected across the tachogenerator output. Set the motor speed to about 100 rev/min as indicated by this voltmeter and the tachogenerator calibration chart. Observe and record the effect of increasing and decreasing the gain. Set the gain to minimum and adjust the reference level to produce a speed of 150 rev/min.

Lightly load the motor drive shaft with finger pressure until the speed falls to about 100 rev/min and note the effect on V_{in}. Leave the reference level as already set and adjust the gain until the speed rises to about 200 rev/min. Now reduce the set speed level until the motor speed falls back to about 150 rev/min. Note the effect on speed and V_{in} as the same finger loading is applied as before.

Repeat the last steps with increasing gain values, recording the effects of finger loading on speed reaction and V_{in}. At close to maximum gain, operation at both high and low speed is likely to be erratic and an oscilloscope will show that V_{in} carries a significant oscillating component. However, the higher gain values should be accompanied by a faster response to the external disturbance.

Exercise 1.4

Using the same system constructed for Exercise 1.3, modify the inverting opamp so that the gain level is relatively much lower. Set this amplifier to maximum gain (i.e. highest speed).

Measure and record the set speed input voltage (call this V_{in}) and the amplifier output voltage (call this V_{out}) at the instant that the motor just begins to turn. Calculate the gain magnitude from V_{out}/V_{in} for a range of set speed voltages in say 0.5 V steps from zero to 5 V and tabulate the results. Plot the graph of gain (vertical) that just causes the motor to turn; this is effectively the *deadband* which is largely due to stiction.

Test questions

1 Refer to Figure 1.6.
   (a) Describe the operation of the system as the slider of R_1 is moved towards the 0 V level.
   (b) Explain the effect on the system if the temperature sensor develops a short-circuit.

23

2 Refer to Figure 1.10.
  (a) Distinguish between the different functions performed by RAM and ROM.
  (b) The oven is operating at an indicated temperature of 95 °C. Describe the effects on the system if a keypad input resets the temperature to 90 °C.

3 Refer to Figure 1.11.
  (a) The setting of R_1 is suddenly moved from zero to the $+10$ V position.
      (i) Describe the subsequent effect on the system.
      (ii) Assuming that the system is critically damped, sketch the power amplifier input waveform whilst the shaft is moving.
  (b) The $+10$ V supply to R_2 suddenly fails and falls to zero. Describe the subsequent reaction of the system.

4 Refer to Figure 1.12.
  (a) State the functions performed by R_1 and R_2.
  (b) Explain the effect on the system if the motor speed rises owing to a reduction in loading.
  (c) Explain the effect on the system if the feedback loop develops an open circuit.

5 (a) Explain why an amplifier may be required in the feedback loop of certain closed-loop control systems.
  (b) Under what conditions may an amplifier be required to drive the final controlling device of a system?

6 (a) Explain the effect of mechanical backlash in a position-control system.
  (b) Explain the effect on system performance caused by an opamp comparator for which the input-offset voltage has been incorrectly set.

2 Rotating machines, relays, solenoids and actuators

Summary

Basic principles, operation and applications of rotating machines, relays, solenoids and actuators, including d.c., stepping, servo and induction motors. Electrical, pneumatic and hydraulic actuators. (Syllabus section 7.2)

Electric motors

The basic principles and rules governing the operation of rotating machines were described in Volume 1 of this series and the reader is referred to this for any necessary revision.

Motors used in control systems may be either d.c.- or a.c.-powered. The d.c. motor has problems associated with its commutating brush gear that generates both contact arcing and radio-frequency interference, and this of course adds to the cost of maintenance and servicing. However, the d.c. motor is very easy to control in both speed and direction of rotation. By comparison, the a.c. motor with its built-in commutation due to a.c. supply is easier to service and, for the same power output, tends to be lighter and smaller, but is more difficult to control. Reducing the supply voltage to the a.c. motor certainly lowers its speed, but it then becomes susceptible to speed variation due to minor changes of loading. The d.c. motor is thus most important to control system engineering.

The important parameter of any motor is its ability to deliver a constant

25

turning moment or *torque* over a range of operational speeds. This is related to its *load regulation* which is described as the ratio

$$\frac{\text{No load speed} - \text{Full load speed}}{\text{Full load speed}}$$

and usually expressed as a percentage.

D.c. motors

The permanent magnet motor as described in Volume 1 finds few applications in a practical environment, in spite of being very easy to control. In most cases, the stationary magnetic field is produced from a separate field winding which is energized from the same source as the armature. Generally, the winding resistance of the armature relative to that of the field is low: of the order of a few ohms. Thus at start-up, there is a large inrush of current. As the motor begins to turn, the armature behaves as a generator, producing an e.m.f. proportional to the rate of turning, but in opposition to the energizing voltage. This back e.m.f. thus causes the running current of the motor to fall to perhaps 10% of its original starting value.

The most common and practical way of using this *split field* concept is the *shunt-wound motor*, in which the armature and field coils are connected in parallel as shown in Figure 2.1. The rotation of this motor can be changed by reversing either the armature or field currents separately. Simply reversing the polarity of the supply voltage reverses both currents simultaneously and results in the motor continuing to run in the original direction. This feature can be readily checked using Fleming's left-hand rule. Often with low-power systems, the motor will be driven via d.c.-coupled push–pull amplifiers.

Motor speed can be varied by one of the two methods indicated. In Figure 2.1 (a), increasing the value of resistor R reduces the field voltage and hence its current. This in turn reduces the back e.m.f. generated in the armature so that the armature current rises and hence increases the motor speed. In Figure 2.1 (b), increasing the value of R simply reduces the armature current and therefore reduces the motor speed.

Field current control requires only the use of a relatively low-power resistor. Since this dissipates little heat, the method is energy-efficient. However, an increased load on the motor would produce a speed reduction that has to be countered by a control action. Since an increase in speed is achieved by lowering the field current and hence the magnetic field strength, the motor torque tends to fall, just at the time an increased torque is needed to meet the demands of the load. By comparison, armature control, which does not suffer from this torque reduction problem, requires the use of a higher power-rating control which dissipates more heat and is less energy-efficient.

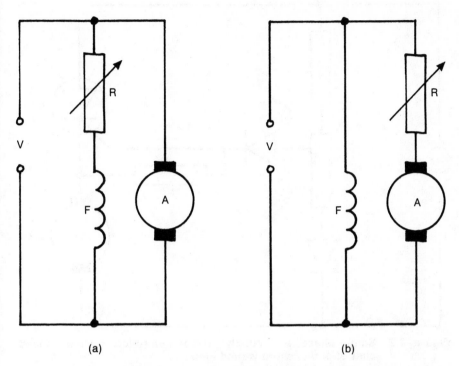

(a)   (b)

Figure 2.1   Shunt-wound d.c. motor speed control by: (a) variation of field current; (b) variation of armature current

In the *series-wound motor*, the field and armature coils are connected in series, but this technique does not find favour in control systems. This motor can easily be reversed as before, but any attempt to use a series resistor to vary the speed results in problems of excessive speed fluctuation with motor loading.

Speed control of d.c. shunt-wound motor

A speed-control technique that can be used with a.c. mains-driven d.c. motors is shown in Figure 2.2. The d.c. feed for the motor is obtained by the half-wave rectification action of the thyristor or silicon-controlled rectifier (SCR). Diode D_1 together with R_1 and R_2 provides a d.c. voltage to trigger the SCR. R_2 also acts as the set speed control. Diode D_2 prevents the motor from short-circuiting the operation of D_1. As R_2 is moved upwards the SCR gate voltage increases, thus allowing the firing voltage to occur earlier in the mains a.c. cycle. The SCR therefore conducts for a longer period during each half cycle and the motor speed increases. The reverse action occurs when R_2 is moved downwards.

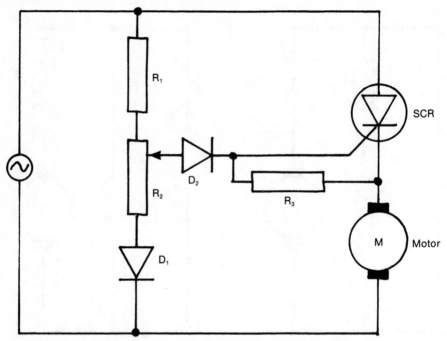

Figure 2.2 Single-phase a.c. supply; silicon-controlled rectifier speed control of d.c. shunt-wound motor

Servicing d.c. motors

After a period of use the brush gear wears, to deposit dust within the motor carcass. This may easily form conductive tracks between brush holders and casing, creating a leakage path to earth, thus robbing the motor of energy and giving rise to a loss of torque. The motor will therefore need periodic stripping and cleaning, replacement of brushes and a light turning of the commutator in a lathe, to restore its original cylindrical shape.

The Hall-effect or brushless d.c. motor

The problems associated with the commutating brush gear of the basic d.c. motor can be resolved by using magnetically controlled semiconductor switches that produce the necessary current reversals. The motor then becomes more reliable, produces less interference and runs more smoothly.

Figure 2.3 shows one particular configuration of such a motor. The two windings W_1 and W_2 are fixed, while the rotating part is formed by a permanent ring magnet, magnetized with three pole pairs. Two Hall generators Hg_1 and Hg_2 are mounted at right angles to each other and spaced about 1 mm from the

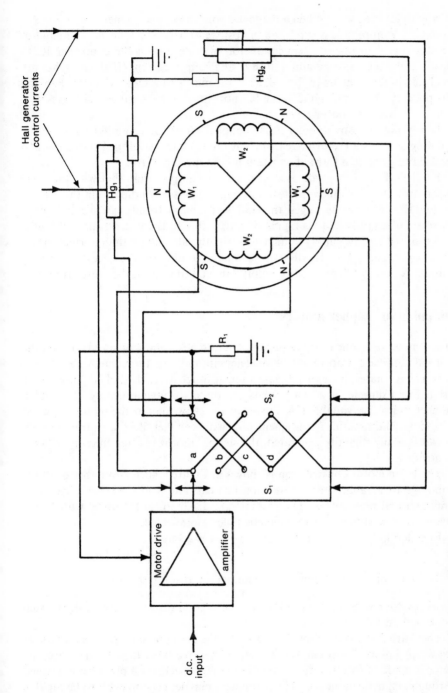

Figure 2.3 Hall-effect d.c. motor

29

periphery of the rotor. When a magnetic pole passes each generator, a pulse of about 0.5 V amplitude is produced of positive or negative polarity. These pulses are then used to operate semiconductor switches within the controller IC to produce the necessary commutation of the supply current. If the switches are operated in the sequence a, b, c, d, a . . . the motor runs clockwise. By changing the polarity of a control line in the IC (not shown), this sequence becomes d, c, b, a, d . . . and the motor reverses.

D.c. power is provided via a d.c.-coupled motor drive amplifier. Since the winding currents all return to earth via R_1, the voltage developed across this can be used to provide a form of constant motor speed control.

Fault-finding in this type of motor is more complex than that with the basic d.c. motor. Not only may faults develop in the motor windings, but the control IC and the motor drive stages, the Hall device bias currents can also fail. Since these are often provided via regulator stages, this adds another source of faults. A motor with a low supply voltage will usually take longer than normal to run up to operating speed. It will then be unable to develop the necessary driving torque. A poorly filtered power supply can lead to jitter in the motor rotation.

Stepping or stepper motors

In a number of applications requiring accurate positioning or speed control, the normal feedback loop might be an encumbrance. In these cases the stepper motor that rotates through a precise angular range for each applied pulse can be used. For example, if a shaft needs to rotate through precisely 750° and a stepper motor is available that moves in 15° steps, then if the motor is pulsed $750/15 = 50$ times, this requirement will have been met. Because a train of such pulses is easily digitally generated, the stepper motor is often microprocessor-controlled.

The basic motor construction is shown in Figure 2.4(a). A number of stator windings are arranged around the motor carcass and wound so that north poles are generated when any given coil is energized. The rotor is formed with a star-shape cross-section and with magnetic poles as indicated.

In general, the *step angle* for such a motor is given by:

$$\frac{360°}{\text{Number of stator windings} \times \text{Number of rotor pole pairs}}$$

Thus for four windings and three pole pairs as shown in Figure 2.4, the step angle will be 30°.

There are two basic stepper motor types, the permanent magnet rotor type as shown in Figure 2.4(a) and the *variable-reluctance* type. In the latter case, the rotor is made of soft iron that is neutrally magnetized, with poles being formed through magnetic induction. The permanent magnet version tends to be capable

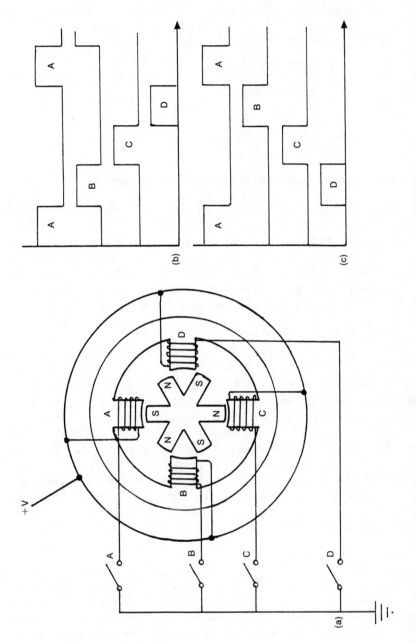

Figure 2.4 The stepping motor: (a) general structure of motor; (b) clockwise rotation sequence; (c) anticlockwise rotation sequence

31

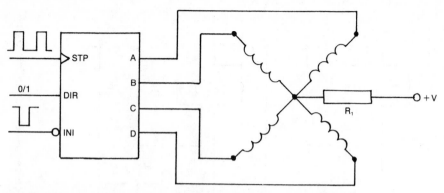

Figure 2.5   Stepping motor with integrated-circuit control

of the highest speed, while the variable-reluctance motor often has the smallest step angle and can operate over a wider speed range.

Referring to Figure 2.4(a), the switches A, B, C, D are closed individually and if A has been closed, a north pole was generated at A so that the rotor takes up the position shown. If B is closed next, the rotor turns so that the nearest south pole ends up opposite to pole B. Thus if the switches are closed in the sequence A, B, C, D, A the motor rotates clockwise (see Figure 2.4(b)). If the switching sequence is changed to A, D, C, B, A the motor will run in the anticlockwise direction (Figure 2.4(c)).

Figure 2.5 indicates the manner in which a stepper motor can be operated with an IC driver device. The input DIR is set to 0 or 1 to control the direction of rotation, the INI (INItialization) line is driven low to turn the rotor into its correct starting position, and the STP input is provided with the stepping pulse train. The power amplifiers within this particular IC connected to A, B, C, D provide current-sinking inputs (i.e. they draw current from coil power source). Resistor R_1 is provided not as a current limiter (although it has that effect), but to improve the motor performance. The stepper motor impedance is highly inductive with a low effective resistance. Its time constant L/R is thus fairly high so that the input pulse will suffer distortion and lower the motor torque. By adding an extra series resistance, the time constant is reduced to $L/(R+R_1)$ to produce less pulse distortion.

Failures in stepper motor systems

The motor itself is fairly robust; apart from mechanical failures, the coils may individually develop open or short circuits. The drive circuits are much more problematic and fault-tracing here should follow conventional low-frequency amplifier-testing procedures. An interesting situation arises if the supply to one winding fails. Suppose this is winding B of Figure 2.4(a) and winding A has just been energized so that the rotor takes up the position shown. Since there is no current through B the rotor will remain stationary during this pulse period. When C is pulsed a north pole is opposite to the winding generating a repulsion effect, but since the forces will be acting in a straight line the rotor will be locked in this position. Now when D is pulsed, the nearest south pole in the rotor will be attracted to this north pole and the motor will turn anticlockwise, rotating through 30°. When A is again pulsed, the rotor north pole will be repelled and the nearest south pole attracted so that the rotor now turns clockwise through 30°. As long as the motor remains energized, the rotor will oscillate between these two positions. If such a motor is running under zero load conditions, it may be noticed that the rotor has enough inertia to carry it over the dead pole so that it continues to rotate but in an erratic manner.

Identification of the faulty position can be made by using an oscilloscope to locate missing pulses. If this line is then disconnected from the motor, it will be possible to detect whether or not the pulse is present at the amplifier output. An open-circuit motor winding can be confirmed using continuity testing. However, short circuits are more difficult, but useful resistance comparisons can be made with the other windings.

A.c. motors

In this type of motor, the power is applied to a stationary field winding or *stator* and it operates by inducing currents in the *rotor* or armature. With the motor built in this way, there is no need for commutating brush gear. Most a.c. induction motors use a *squirrel-cage* rotor, so described because of the way in which its conductors are arranged. The general construction is indicated in Figure 2.6, where the main body is made up from discs of ferromagnetic iron. Each lamination is insulated from its neighbour in the same way as a transformer core to minimize the effects of eddy currents. Slots are cut in the cylindrical structure and these carry fairly large cross-sectioned conductor bars of either aluminium or copper. These are all connected to two conducting end-rings so that a series of current loops are formed. Because of the high resistance across the length of the armature, there is no great electrical stress on the conductors-to-core insulation. When this structure rotates relative to a magnetic field, currents are induced in the loops and these set up secondary magnetic fields. The reaction between these two fields is responsible for the resulting rotation.

Single-phase a.c. induction motor

A squirrel-cage rotor is mounted in bearings so that it is free to rotate in a laminated iron frame similar to that shown in Figure 2.7. One end of the frame carries the single field winding which is connected to an a.c. power source. Two

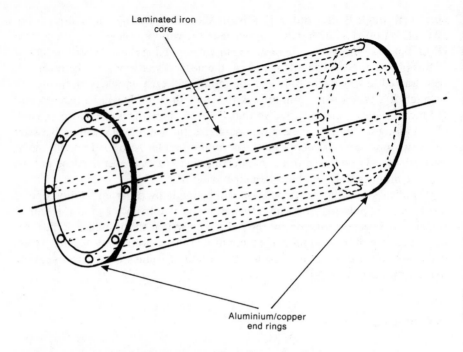

Laminated iron core

Aluminium/copper end rings

Figure 2.6   Squirrel-cage rotor assembly

sets of *shading coils* are added to the frame as indicated. These represent short-circuited turns in which eddy currents can flow to produce alternating magnetic fields. These tend to oppose the main magnetic field produced by the a.c. supply, so that the field builds up to a peak in different parts of the periphery of the rotor aperture at different times. The overall effect is to produce a magnetic field that appears to rotate around the aperture. The rotating field cuts the rotor conductor bars to induce the currents that generate the secondary magnetic field. The reaction between the two fields creates an effect where the rotor tries to follow the rotating field. The rotor can never reach the same speed as the magnetic field. If it did, there would be no relative motion to induce the rotor currents and the motor would produce zero torque. Therefore there must always be some *slip* between the rotor speed and the *synchronous* speed of the field, and this is expressed as a proportion of the synchronous speed as follows. If a motor driven from a 50 Hz supply runs at a speed of 2700 rev/min, the slippage is $3000 - 2700 = 300$ rev/min or $300/3000 = 0.1$ or 10%

The single-phase induction motor finds very few applications in control engineering because of its poor speed/voltage characteristic and the fact that, once constructed, it cannot be made to run in reverse. Variable-speed operation is usually achieved by using a variable-frequency power supply. Changing the

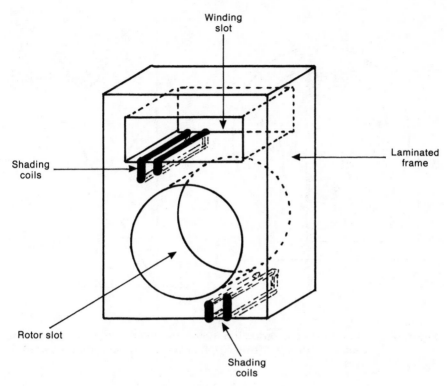

Figure 2.7   A.c. induction motor frame

supply voltage varies the motor speed but introduces an unacceptable speed/ torque characteristic.

Split-phase a.c. motor

Figure 2.8(a) represents the stator of this type of motor without the rotor installed. The pairs of windings are energized from a.c. sources V_1 and V_2 that are 90° out of phase with each other. The resulting currents, shown in Figure 2.8(b), increase and decrease in an out-of-phase manner and create alternating magnetic fields acting horizontally and vertically across the stator frame. The net magnetic flux within the stator is thus the phasor or vector sum of these two components. At an instant when I_1 is at maximum and I_2 is zero, the net magnetic field will act vertically. Ninety degrees later, when I_1 has fallen to zero, I_2 will be a maximum and the net field will act horizontally. At periods in between, the net flux will tend to rotate between these two extremes. This action continues over the remaining part of the a.c. cycle, so that the net magnetic field rotates around the rotor aperture.

If a squirrel-cage rotor is mounted within the frame, the induced currents will

35

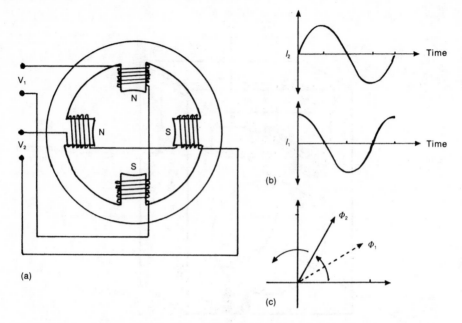

Figure 2.8   Split-phase a.c. induction motor and rotating field: (a) poles and winding structure; (b) split-phase currents; (c) rotating magnetic field

cause the rotor to follow the rotating magnetic field in a manner similar to that of the single-phase induction motor. The *synchronous speed* of the split-phase induction motor is given by:

$$\frac{\text{Power supply frequency}}{\text{Number of pole pairs in stator winding}}$$

For the motor shown in Figure 2.8 with two pole pairs and driven by 50 Hz supply, the synchronous speed will be 50 rev/s/2 or 3000/2 = 1500 rev/min.

At zero load there will be practically no slippage but this will increase with loading, up to about 3–8% depending upon the particular motor.

Generating the rotating magnetic field

By connecting a low-reactance capacitor (typically several μF) in series with winding 1 of Figure 2.8(a), the current I_1 will lead I_2 by nearly 90°. The motor will then run in an anticlockwise direction. If the capacitor is switched in series with the second winding, the magnetic fluxes will cause the motor to reverse. This is shown schematically in Figure 2.9.

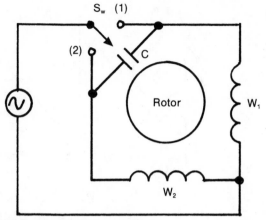

Figure 2.9   Split-phase a.c. motor control

Single phasing

Some split-phase motors are designed to start up with a series capacitor in one lead. When the motor has run up to speed, a centrifugal switch operates to open-circuit the winding (the *starting winding*) and the motor continues to operate on the single *running winding*.

Servo motors

Servo-control systems are required when an object that has to be moved is either too large, too heavy, inaccessible, or contained in a dangerous environment. A servo system is one in which the final system variable requires some mechanical movement. The controlling unit is then described as a servo motor.

Because servo motors are required to be able to respond rapidly to changing commands, the rotor should have a very low inertia. This is achieved by making its diameter small and as light as possible. The loss of torque that this produces is countered by increasing lengths of the conductors. Thus servo motors have relatively long thin rotors with the conductors made of aluminium.

Ideally these motors should have a linear voltage/speed characteristic and provide a constant torque. For high-power applications, the d.c. servo motor tends to be more energy-efficient, so that a.c. servo motors are often used for low-power applications.

D.c. servo motors

These are based on the shunt-wound motor, but operate with one winding supplied from a fixed source and the other under the control of the amplified

37

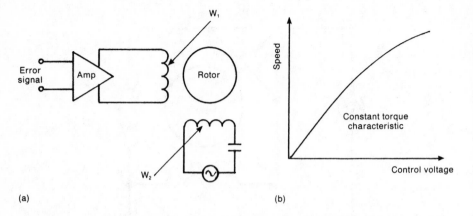

Figure 2.10   (a) Control of a.c. servo motor; (b) voltage/speed characteristic

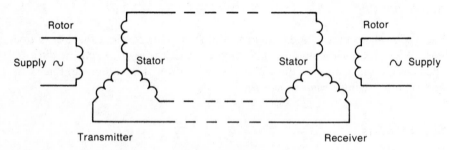

Figure 2.11   A selsyn system (schematic)

error signal. Both armature and field speed control can be used, but the latter which requires a smaller drive current is more popular.

A.c. servo motors

These motors are always based on the split-field concept and operate from a fixed and a controlled power supply in the manner shown in Figure 2.10(a). The amplified error signal and the fixed supply frequencies must be synchronous otherwise the motor will fail to run correctly. Figure 2.10(b) indicates that the speed/voltage characteristic for constant torque is fairly linear. To prevent the motor trying to *single-phase* when the control voltage falls to zero, the rotor conductor bars are made to have a higher series resistance than would be found in the conventional split-phase motor.

The *selsyn* position-indicating and transmission system is an old-fashioned non-electronic system which is still used. A selsyn is constructed like an a.c. motor, with a three-phase stator and a two-phase rotor. Although Figure 2.11

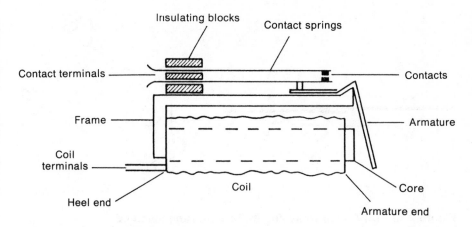

Figure 2.12   Electromagnetic relay

shows the stator windings star-connected, they may alternatively be connected in delta configuration.

Both rotors are connected to the same a.c. supply (typically 400 Hz) so that the supply to both is constantly in phase. The stators are connected to one another as shown. When the shaft of one rotor is turned, the voltages induced in its stator will be transmitted to the other stator and will cause the rotor of that selsyn to move to the same position as the first.

Relays

A relay is an electromagnetical device often used as a remotely controlled switch in power circuits. A typical example of one type is shown in Figure 2.12.

A current flowing through the coil causes the core to become magnetized and attract the armature. This movement operates switch contacts against contact spring pressure, to enable other circuits to be made or broken. Since there is no electrical contact between the coil and the switch contracts, there is complete isolation between the two parts of the circuit.

When the current through the coil is interrupted, the magnetic field collapses and the armature is forced to return to its former position by the tension in the contact springs. Typical operate and release times for such a relay average about 10 ms and 7 ms respectively, the release time being invariably the shorter of the two. In some types of relay, the release time can be shortened by including a small nonmagnetic stud or screw (sometimes adjustable) that prevents the armature from making a metallic contact with the core.

The *operate current* has to be high enough to generate sufficient magnetomotive force (m.m.f.) to overcome the *reluctance* of the air gap to become

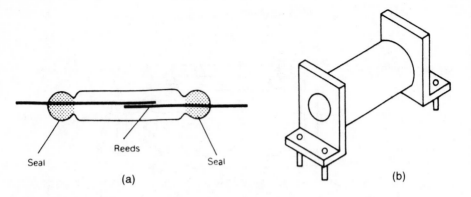

Figure 2.13   (a) A reed relay and (b) its operating solenoid

magnetized. When operated, this air gap disappears and so the *holding current* needed to sustain operation is considerably lower.

Although a relay is current-operated, it is usually specified either by its operating power or voltage. Since its coil resistance is also commonly quoted, it is possible to determine the operate current. By comparison, the relay designer usually works from the basis of the m.m.f. in ampere-turns (AT) needed to operate the relay. The following example usefully demonstrates the relationship between these parameters. A 24 V relay with a coil of 2000 turns and 500 Ω resistance has an operate current of 24/500 = 12 mA, an operate power of 12 mA $\times$ 24 V = 288 mW and an m.m.f. of 2000 $\times$ 24 mA = 48 AT.

The relay contact size and material depend upon the particular application. Generally, small precious-metal contacts of gold, platinum, or palladium that provide a contact resistance of about 50 mΩ are used for light-current circuits. For power-switching applications, larger tungsten contacts are commonly used.

Relay contact operation is sometimes characterized in the following manner;

normally open — form A;
normally closed — form B;
change-over — form C.

A *reed relay* consists of a pair of small metal leaves, or reeds, sealed into a glass tube and pulled into or released out of contact with one another by the application or removal of a magnetic field generated by a d.c. current flowing in a solenoid wound round the tube. Figure 2.13(a) shows a typical such relay, with the solenoid through which the tube is passed shown in (b).

Reed relays have the following advantages compared to relays of the armature type:

1   *Small size*, with moving parts of low mass. Typical operating times as low as 1 ms and release times of 0.2 ms can therefore be obtained.

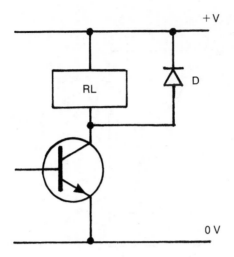

Figure 2.14   Suppression of back e.m.f.

2   *Longer working life*, because the contacts are sealed against the intrusion of dirt and atmospheric impurities.
3   *Easy replacement of contacts*, since the glass tube containing the relay can be removed from the solenoid and replaced by a new one.
4   Much *lower operating power* is required.
5   Reed switches can be *operated directly by magnets*, either as push-button switches or so that the exact position of a wheel or arm carrying a permanent magnet can be sensed by the closure of reed contacts.
6   High current reeds contain a pool of mercury which provides a *low contact resistance*.

When either of these types of relay is driven by a transistor or an IC, some form of suppressor circuit is required to avoid damage to the semiconductors from the large surge of voltage (the *back e.m.f.*) which is generated when the current is switched off. A typical such suppression circuit containing a diode is shown in Figure 2.14.

Latched relays and circuits

A *latching relay* is one that can be switched on by a pulse of current. It will then remain on until it is switched off by the application of a current pulse of the opposite polarity. Such devices often find applications in motor-switching circuits.

Mechanical latching devices rely on a spring-loaded latch to lock the armature in place after the magnetic action has produced closure. A push-button, or a second coil and armature is then needed to release the latch so that the relay can return to its de-energized position.

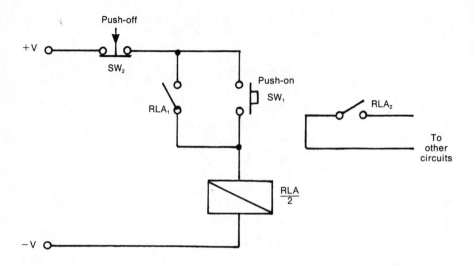

Figure 2.15   A latching circuit

Remanence relays either have a small permanent magnetic sleeve mounted on the core, or the core is made of a special ferrous material which retains some magnetism from a current pulse. Once operated, the relay remains energized in a power-free mode. Release is obtained by the application of a pulse of the reverse polarity. Operating pulse durations vary between about 10 ms and 20 ms. For a.c. operation, the remanence relay is often driven via series rectifier diodes.

Electrical latching circuits similar to that shown in Figure 2.15 are more commonly used for these applications. When the switch SW_1 is closed, the relay becomes energized; contacts RLA_1 and RLA_2 close so that, when SW_1 is released, the coil remains energized. The circuit will remain latched until released by the operation of SW_2. The use of a relay is indicated on the diagram by two symbols, one representing the coil, the other the contacts. The two symbols often appear in widely separated parts of the circuit diagram, and the drawing convention is therefore known as the *detached-contact system*, of which Figure 2.15 represents a simple example.

A latching d.c. motor-control circuit is shown in Figure 2.16 but drawn as a *ladder diagram*: a technique commonly used for relay logic circuits. When push-button P_1 is closed, the relay coil is energized and contacts A_1 and A_2 make. The closure of A_2 causes the motor to run, while contact A_1 acts as the latch. The motor can be stopped by closing P_2 for a period greater than about 20 ms. This action short-circuits the relay coil and causes it to de-energize. R_1 is included to allow a lower-voltage relay to be used from the same supply as the motor and to limit the current flowing through the various contacts.

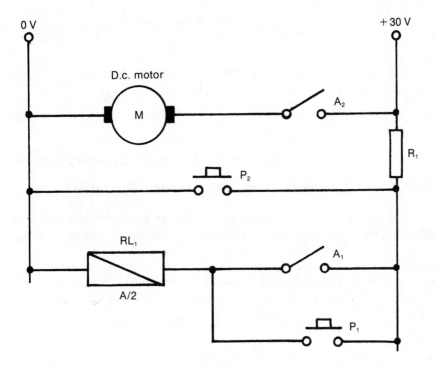

Figure 2.16   D.c. motor control circuit

Detached contact systems

The coil of a relay is symbolized by a rectangular box, which can (but need not) carry coding to indicate the characteristics of the relay. The coil is identified by the letters RL, with the letter or number of the relay following. Underneath, there appears a digit giving the number of contacts on the relay.

Every contact set is shown in the part of the circuit to which it belongs, identified by the letter RL, the letter or number of the relay, and the number assigned to that contact. The convention can be seen in use in Figure 2.17 where all the contacts are shown in the de-energized state of the coil. Figure 2.18 shows some of the special symbols referred to above.

Slugged relays

The basic operate and release times of relays can be modified by various methods. For example, the shunt diode used in Figure 2.14 to suppress the back e.m.f. maintains a current flow through the relay coil for a short period after switch-off. The relay thus becomes slow to release.

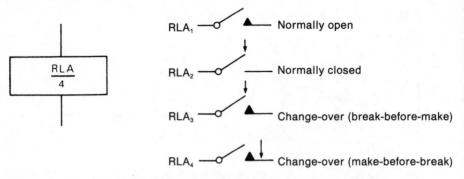

Figure 2.17   The detached-contact system of representing relays

A thick cylindrical copper ring (a slug) may also be fitted to one end of the coil core where it acts as a short-circuited turn of very low resistance. This uses energy obtained from the changing magnetic field at switch-on and switch-off to modify the relay characteristics. If a slug is fitted to the armature end, the relay becomes both slow to make and release. By comparison, if the slug is fitted to the heel end there is little effect on the operate time, but the relay becomes slow to release.

A.c. relays

Any d.c. relay may be operated from an a.c. source using a series rectifier diode. However, a slugged slow-to-release relay will also operate directly from a.c. In many cases, the appearance of a.c. and d.c. relays is very similar; the only difference is the small copper washer fitted close to the armature end to act as a slug or shading coil.

Contactors

These are special relays designed for high-power switching and often driven from a.c. supplies. For single-phase operation, these devices will usually be equipped with core-fitted shading coils. However, three-phase contactors do not require this slugging because the average or effective magnetic flux does not fall to zero.

Solid-state relays

These are semiconductor devices that usually draw their operating power from the supplies that they are intended to switch. The basic construction follows IC techniques and the circuits consist of a high-speed amplifier input, followed by a high-speed flip-flop stage driving power-amplifier switches. Operating voltages

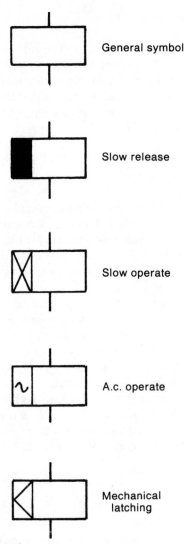

Figure 2.18 Relay symbols

and currents range from about 3 to 36 V and from 2 to 40 mA respectively. A few devices are capable of switching voltages in the order of 300 V at several amps of current. Leakage currents are very small: in the order of 5 mA maximum. The output resistance is significantly higher than the typical 50 mΩ of the electromagnetic relay. However, because the electronic circuit has negligible self-inductance, the switching speeds are measured in microseconds compared to the milliseconds of the electromechanical device.

45

Faults in relay logic circuits

Faults in relay circuits commonly fall into two categories: mechanical problems involving wear and tear of contacts, and open or short circuits in the operating coils. Because relay servicing is a highly skilled task, in both cases the most economical approach is to replace the suspect devices. In general, fault-finding in these circuits tends to follow digital techniques in the switched part of the system, plus measuring coil voltages/currents in the drive sections.

Solenoids or solenoid valves

Basically, a solenoid is the coil part of an electromagnetic relay except that the core is allowed to slide within the coil former. In the de-energized state, the core is spring-loaded so that it rests only partially within the coil and its magnetic influence. The resulting movement of the core when the coil is energized is used to open or close a valve that in turn controls the flow of some product through a system and with an on–off action.

These devices may be d.c.- or a.c.-operated with the latter version often employing the shading coil concept to overcome the alternating magnetic effect of the power supply. The core of an a.c.-operated solenoid is often laminated to minimize the effects of eddy currents. As with the electromagnetic relay, the hold current is much less than the operate current, which reduces as the core is attracted further into the hollow coil former.

Faults with solenoids are usually associated with open- or short-circuited coils. These problems often arise because of a core that sticks part-way into the coil. This causes the solenoid to pass the larger energizing current for long periods owing to the lower coil inductance. This results in overheating and eventual burnout.

Actuators

In systems involved with positional control, the link between the electrical/electronic components and the ultimate controller is performed by an actuator. In general terms, this device provides either rotary or lineary motion. For the former, one of the various types of electric motor is often used, with the stepper motor being particularly suited to small angular movements. For the more continuous type of movement, pneumatic or hydraulic motors may be employed.

For linear motion, the piston and cylinder concept may be employed, using either fluid pressure or a vacuum as the operating medium. Alternatively, a linear motion can be achieved by using a motor to drive a threaded lead screw

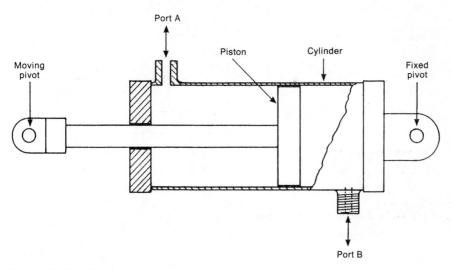

Figure 2.19   Linear actuator

and nut mechanism (screw-jack principle), or by using a rack-and-pinion type gearing.

Whatever type of action is employed, this mechanical system will need to be equipped with limit switches to prevent the mechanism from being overdriven and creating damage. For very large rotary valves, the inertia or stiction may be too great to be conveniently handled by an electric motor. In this case, it is more appropriate to use a hydraulic motor that tends to have a greater starting torque relative to the same size of electric motor.

Figure 2.19 shows the general construction of one type of linear actuator. This is operated either from fluid pressure (air or oil) or a vacuum. Pressure entering through one port causes the piston to move, exhausting the surplus fluid from the other port. Such devices are capable of operating over a very wide range of working stroke lengths and can deliver considerable thrust between the end links. Figure 2.20 shows the way in which a linear actuator can be controlled. A shuttle valve is used to direct the fluid pressure into the appropriate port and this is controlled by the closed-loop system. In this example, if the shuttle valve moves to the right under system feedback control, pressure is fed into the left-hand side of the cylinder and the piston is forced to the right. The speed with which this movement occurs depends upon the extent of the movement of the controlling shuttle valve. Excess pressure from the right-hand side of the cylinder is exhausted through the right-hand path ducting. Such a system has considerable mechanical advantage or gain. Only a small amount of effort is needed to drive the shuttle valve, but this allows the fluid pressure input to be converted into considerable mechanical thrust by the piston/cylinder assembly.

47

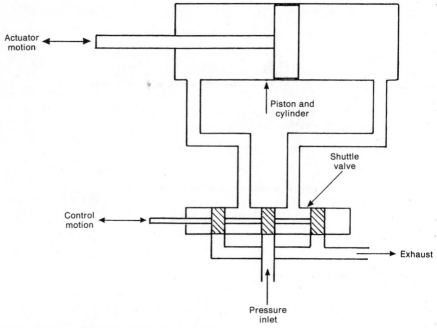

Figure 2.20   Control of linear actuator

Rotary actuators based on the same concept may also be used. In this case, the cylinder is constructed in an annular form, with the piston replaced by a rotary vane. This is attached to a pivotal shaft that provides the ultimate rotary control action over a maximum range of about 280°. These devices generate a high starting torque and can be used to operate bell crank mechanisms, butterfly and gate control valves, screw clamps and many other similar final controllers.

A torque doubling can be achieved by dividing the annular chamber into two sections and using a pair of coupled vanes. In this case, however, the control range is restricted to about 100°.

Since air is very compressible, pneumatic actuators are commonly used only for low-power applications. By comparison, hydraulic actuators are most suitable for high-power applications and in environments such as chemical, explosive and mining that are hostile to electrical motors. Good examples of this are automotive and earth-moving equipment applications.

Exercise 2.1

Measure the d.c. armature resistance R of a small shunt-wound motor. Connect a current meter in series with the armature winding and connect the motor to a low d.c. voltage (V) source. With the motor running, record the armature current I. The initial motor current at start-up must have been V/R, but has fallen to I. Calculate $IR = v$. Now $V - v$ must be the back e.m.f. produced by the armature rotation.

Exercise 2.2

By reversing the field and armature windings singly and then together, investigate the possible methods of making the d.c. motor of Exercise 2.1 run in both directions.

Exercise 2.3

Speed control of the d.c. motor using a change of armature current produces logical and expected results. The effect of the field control method is less obvious, however. Connect a current meter and a suitable variable resistance in series with the field winding and a second current meter in series with the armature. Run the motor from a suitable d.c. source and vary the value of the field resistance, noting how the motor changes speed. Note also the effect that speed variation has on the armature current.

Exercise 2.4

Using one of the proprietary control system training units, set up a stepper motor experiment. Note how the motor can be driven in both directions and at various speeds. Now disconnect one of the pulse feed lines to the motor. Note the effect that this has over a wide range of speeds and with various motor loadings.

Test questions

1 Refer to Figure 2.21.
   (a) State two methods by which this motor can be made to rotate in opposite directions.
   (b) Describe two methods by which the motor speed can be made to vary.
   (c) Why is the series-wound d.c. motor unsuitable for industrial applications?

2 Refer to Figure 2.22.
   (a) Describe the sequence of events as P_1 is pressed.
   (b) Describe the sequence of events when P_2 is pressed.
   (c) What functions are performed by D_1 and R_1?
   (d) When the motor is running a power failure occurs so that the supply

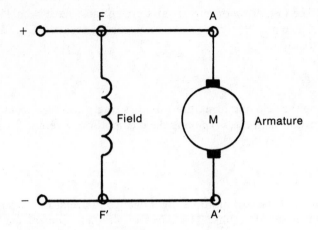

Figure 2.21   Diagram for test question 1

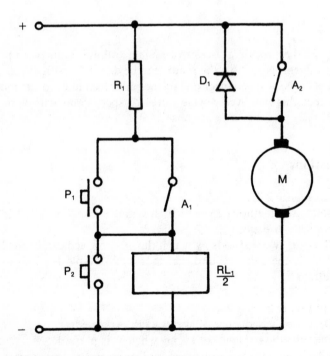

Figure 2.22   Diagram for test question 2

fails for about 1 s before being restored. Describe what happens during this period and immediately after the power is restored.

3 (a) What is the rotational speed of a split-phase a.c. motor with a three-pole-pair stator winding when driven from a 50 Hz supply?

(b) A stepper motor has a rotor of three pole pairs and eight stator poles. Calculate its step angle.

(c) The motor in (b) is required to rotate precisely through 840°. Calculate the number of pulses needed.

4 Describe the features that distinguish a d.c. servo motor from its conventional motive power counterpart.

5 For a shunt-wound d.c. motor describe the ideal characteristics for:
(a) torque/speed characteristic for constant armature voltage;
(b) speed/voltage characteristic for constant torque.

6 Distinguish between the functions performed by solenoids, relays, contactors and actuators.

3 Measurements and instrumentation

Summary

Principles, applications and limitations of chart recorders, instrumentation recorders, oscilloscopes, function generators, universal bridges and counter/timers. Determination of specific types of measurement. (Syllabus section 7.3)

Introduction

Display devices are designed to convert instrumentation signals into a form that is readily useful to a human observer. Devices such as pointer instruments and cathode-ray tubes produce displays that require direct interpretation of events that are current. By comparison, photographic and similar displays provide a permanent record of an event that occurred at some time in the past. Both types play a useful role in system maintenance.

Analogue displays require the human operator to interpret the readings to an acceptable degree of accuracy. In the case of a digital display, the readings have already been suitably approximated during the analogue-to-digital conversion process. Thus with both types of instrument, it is important to recognize this problem. Therefore instruments need to be chosen to give:

1 an acceptable degree of accuracy;
2 ease of reading and interpreting the display;
3 readings that are consistent and repeatable.

52

Instruments are available that have response times varying from a few nanoseconds to several seconds. In general, electrical/electronic devices tend to be more flexible, capable of handling a wider range of signal types and with a more acceptable frequency/time response.

Normally a system transducer will be chosen that provides an output that is proportional to the quantity being measured. Having taken this step, it is important to ensure that the chosen measuring instrument does not destroy this linearity. A recording device that is designed to handle slowly changing values should also be able to respond to sudden disturbances or transient effects. Excessive instrument damping will cause such events to be missed.

Accuracy and precision

As indicated above, all measuring devices introduce some error which can be expressed as

$$\frac{\text{Indicated value} - \text{True value}}{\text{True value}} \times 100\%$$

or

$$\frac{\text{Indicated value} - \text{True value}}{\text{Full scale value}} \times 100\%$$

Precision refers to measurement repeatability in the following manner:

High accuracy/high precision: all measured values will be closely grouped together near to the desired average value.
Low accuracy/high precision: all values will be grouped together but spread over a wider range.
Low accuracy/low precision: values will be scattered over a wide range.

Chart recorders

In addition to using ink-type capillary pens and normal paper, these devices can also use specially sensitive paper as the recording medium to provide two-dimensional plots of the values to be recorded. The range of instruments includes those that respond to the pressure or heat provided by a stylus or reflected electromagnetic radiation (usually ultraviolet).

Ultraviolet (UV) galvanometer recorder

The basic principles and construction involved in this type of recorder are shown in Figure 3.1. The galvanometer (galvo) is based on the moving-coil

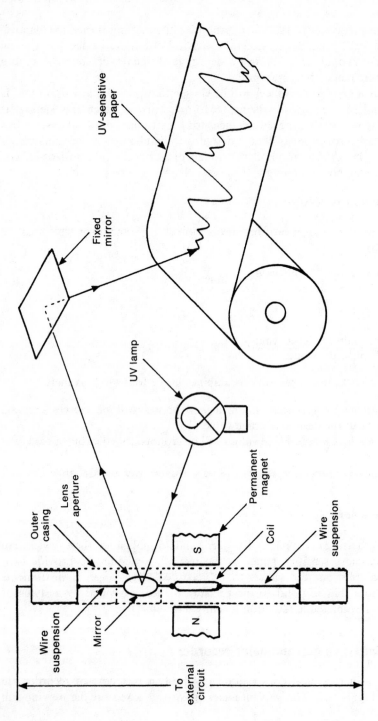

Figure 3.1   UV recorder system

principle to provide the deflection of the small mirror that replaces the conventional pointer. This provides scale indication by the reflection of a UV light beam in the manner shown. In this case, the coil is suspended by two wires that form torsional springs whose twisting action also provides the normal restoring force. To provide damping, the lower suspension wire passes through a capillary tube containing an oil drop. The cylindrical structure is provided by encasing the mechanism within a nonmagnetic metallic tube. This carries a small aperture and lens through which the mirror acts. Using this form of structure, several galvos can be mounted within a common magnet block, producing an instrument capable of handling up to 25 separate channels.

To provide a scale that can be read accurately and easily requires wide spacing of the meter graduations: therefore a long pointer is necessary. With the galvo, this effect is achieved by folding the light beam using a number of fixed mirrors. By using this technique, effective optical pointer lengths up to about 400 mm can be produced.

The ultraviolet source is normally provided by a high-pressure mercury-vapour lamp, typically of 50–100 W rating. Where the reflected energy impinges on the sensitive paper, it leaves a permanent trace representative of the quantity being measured. The timebase of this recording system is controlled by the paper speed and this may vary from about 1 mm/min to 10 m/min.

Because of the natural resonance of the suspension, each galvo has a restricted frequency range. Typically a manufacturer's stock line covering from d.c. to about 15 kHz would be met by ten galvos.

In general, the higher-frequency operation requires the use of a stiffer suspension so that sensitivity falls as frequency rises. The sensitivity may be quoted in two ways: for example, either as 2 cm/mA or 0.5 mA/cm. Typical maximum currents that can be measured range from about 5 mA to 75 mA and coil resistances vary from about 50 to 100 Ω.

Although UV galvo recorders need to be relatively large in order to ensure rigid mounting of the mirrors, multichannel operation is easily achieved.

Servicing problems

Apart from the periodic lamp replacements and paper-drive mechanism lubrication, these instruments are very reliable. Transportation and movement provide the major hazards to mirror positioning and galvo safety and a clamping mechanism is usually provided to prevent damage under these circumstances.

Potentiometric or servo-controlled pen recorder

In this instrument, a servo-controlled pen is used to produce the trace on a continuously moving paper. The pen is usually ink-fed by capillary action.

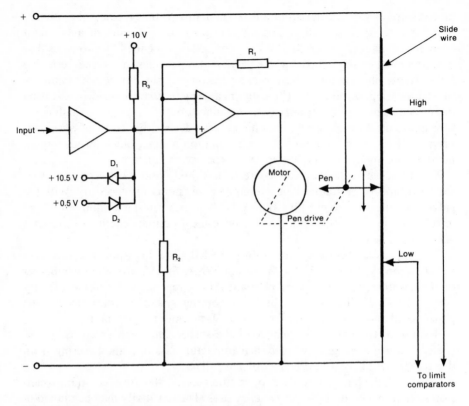

Figure 3.2 Potentiometer pen recorder

Figure 3.2 shows the general arrangement of the electronic control circuit. The pen is driven across the width of the moving paper by the motor and, at the same time, the pen mechanism tracks across a slide-wire resistance. A voltage from this potentiometer is fed via the potential divider network R_1 and R_2 into the inverting input of the comparator. The signal to be recorded is fed via a separate amplifier designed to provide gain and impedance matching to the non-inverting input. The comparator then provides the closed-loop-controlled drive for the pen motor so that the pen follows the slide-wire voltage and the input signal. The time axis is controlled by the use of a constant-speed synchronous motor used to provide the paper travel.

The diode network D_1, D_2 and R_3 forms a limiter circuit to prevent the system from being overdriven by too large an input signal. This automatically clips the non-inverting input signal to the 0 V and 10 V levels. Two further slide-wire voltages are available and these are used, after comparison with 0 V and 10 V supply levels, to provide high- and low-level alarms.

Like all closed-loop control systems, this recorder has a dead band that represents the smallest signal necessary to overcome the motor and mechanism friction. Typically the dead band may be in the order of $\pm 0.25\%$ of maximum deflection. The drive mechanism is also relatively slow, taking as much as 400 ms to reach full-scale deflection.

Typical low input signal level depends upon the degree of amplification provided, but is often as low as 10 mV. Paper speed varies from about 5 mm/h up to 3.5 m/h. Typical multichannel operation of these recorders is restricted to about four pens maximum and these are often employed for continuous environmental monitoring.

Servicing problems

The weak points of this particular type of instrument are the mechanical parts associated with the pen-drive motor, pen guides, pulleys and cables. Electrically, the contact resistance with the slide wire can generate noise if dirt or dust is allowed into the casing. This will be evident by spurious peaks appearing on a trace provided from a test waveform.

X–Y plotter

This version of the chart recorder uses two servo systems to control the position and writing of the pen across the two axes whilst the paper remains stationary.

The pen carriage moves along the y axis on a runner attached to the *gantry*. The gantry itself can traverse the x axis along similar runners provided in the instrument casing. This general construction is indicated in Figure 3.3. A range of x and y input voltages therefore drives the pen over a two dimensional plot. In addition, most x–y plotters are provided with a timebase circuit to allow conventional y/t plots to be produced.

Since this instrument has a relatively slow rate of response due to the inertia of the mechanical mechanism, it is only useful for plotting slowly changing parameters with frequencies as low as 1 Hz. Because the gantry has a greater inertia than the pen carrier, the response time for the y axis will be the shorter of the two. For an A4-sized plot, the times taken for full-scale travel along the x and y axes are of the order of 200 ms and 400 ms respectively. The pen slew rate is therefore the phasor sum of the maximum x and y velocities as follows. If the maximum x and y velocities are 2 m/s and 1.5 m/s respectively, the slew rate is $\sqrt{(2^2 + 1.5^2)} = 2.5$ m/s.

Input impedances in the order of 10 MΩ are common, with an input sensitivity of around 100 mV/cm. Linearity and repeatability are generally better than 0.1% of full-scale deflection.

57

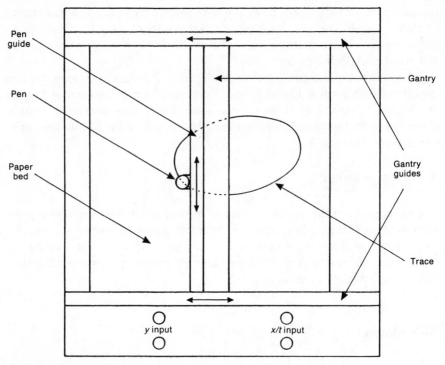

Figure 3.3   X–Y plotter

Servicing problems

Again, the weak points are associated with the pen-drive mechanism. This needs periodic cleaning to remove accumulated dust, and careful lubrication. From the electronics point of view, the problems will be similar to those of the servo-controlled chart recorder.

Instrumentation tape recorder

This device works on the same principle as the audio recorder system described in Volume 1 of this series and the reader is referred to this for any necessary revision.

Magnetic tape forms a convenient storage medium for large amounts of data, particularly that which needs to be made available for later analysis. Technological developments that have been made with the compact audio cassette now make this technique very suitable for industrial applications. In fact, the concept of helical cassette recording, used extensively for video applications, has also been applied to instrumentation work. This system provides a very large data-storage space with a very wide bandwidth available for recording either analogue or digital data. The disadvantage of the tape medium lies in the serial search that has to be made for any particular data item. The problem can be alleviated to some extent by adding a form of timecode as an index along a separate track. This feature can easily be achieved with the ½ in video cassette medium.

The method of recording either analogue or digital signals direct to tape finds few applications; the distortion and noise that would result on playback are unacceptable. The standard audio method of combining the data to be recorded with a bias frequency may also be used for instrumentation purposes. This provides a bandwidth of up to 15 kHz and an acceptable signal-to-noise ratio for analogue data, plus digital bit rates up to about 7.5 kbit/s. By using the helical video recording concept, a bandwidth of up to 5 MHz is available for analogue data, with a corresponding increase for digital data rates.

Frequency modulation (FM) is often used for analogue data recording using a carrier of around 400 kHz modulated to a maximum deviation of 40–50%. Since any amplitude variations such as noise or distortion will be removed by limiters on replay, the signal-to-noise ratio can be high. For the recording of digital data, a form of FM is commonly used which is described as *frequency shift keying* (FSK). A pair of frequencies are selected so that one represents logic 1 and the other logic 0. These frequencies may or may not have an exact harmonic relationship.

Servicing problems

Many of the difficulties are associated with the tape-transport mechanism. It is important that the tape path, guides and heads are maintained in a clean and unworn state. Lubrication needs to be applied very sparingly as oils may easily find their way into areas that rely on friction for drive purposes. A further common problem arises with the tape-drive motors. Wear and tear can give rise to noisy bearings, changes in loading on the motor and consequently changes of motor speed. Since motor speed has a direct effect on the longitudinal tape speed, it is important that this is periodically checked. The electronics problems tend to be similar to those found in normal audio equipment.

Oscilloscope

The principles of operation and application of these instruments were described in Volume 2 Part 1 of this series. The reader is thus referred to this for any necessary revision.

Characteristics of the CRO

Since the cathode-ray oscilloscope (CRO or scope) plots one variable y against another x (or time t), it produces diagrams in the manner of the x–y plotter. However, since the writing medium is an electron beam of negligible mass and inertia, the CRO has a very much faster response to changing signal levels. This response is usually measured in terms of the *rise time* of the displayed waveform. Rise time is defined as the time taken for the waveform to rise (or fall) between the 10% and 90% levels. Rise times in the order of a few tens of nanoseconds, together with a bandwidth exceeding 100 MHz, can readily be achieved.

The visual display is supported by a scribed and sometimes illuminated graticule. This allows fairly accurate assessments of amplitude, phase relationship and time to be made. In addition, with experience it is possible to obtain a reasonable assessment of any distortion found in a waveform.

Because the instrumentation CRO is normally fitted with an electrostatic deflection cathode-ray tube (CRT), the scope amplifier system has a very high input impedance. Typical values are in the order of 10 MΩ in parallel with a self-capacitance of 20 pF. Typical basic beam-deflection sensitivities, which are accurately known for each tube, vary between 0.02 and 0.05 cm/V.

Each scope type is commonly available with a range of alternate CRTs, each with a different persistence of illumination and colour. The following is a useful guide:

Persistence	Colour	General application
Long persistence	Orange	Low-frequency displays
Medium persistence	Green	General-purpose displays
Short persistence	Blue	High-frequency displays

To overcome the transient nature of the display, the CRO can be fitted with a camera attachment to provide a permanent record.

To ensure that the trace starts at the same corresponding point in each cycle and produces a stationary display, the timebase is equipped with a *trigger* circuit. This may be driven from the work signal being applied to the y input or from an external source, the latter often being necessary if the input signal level is small. The internal trigger point is normally level-dependent and switchable for positive- or negative-going signal transitions.

For multichannel operation with a single-beam CRT, the CRO can function in one of two modes, *chopped* or *alternate*. In the chopped mode, the beam is rapidly switched between the two channels to provide a double-trace display, and is limited to relatively low frequencies. Switching high-frequency signals in this manner produces unacceptable gaps in the displayed waveform. In the alternate mode, one sweep is used for each channel alternately, but at the expense of reduced trace brightness. These problems do not arise with genuine double-beam CRTs, but these scopes may be adapted in this manner to provide four-channel operation.

Attenuator probes are available which allow signals to be displayed that are of larger amplitude than can be handled by the internal y attenuator. These are normally switchable with two ranges of $\times 1$ and $\times 10$. However, these need to be calibrated periodically to maintain their high-frequency response and the square shape of a test waveform.

Measurements with the CRO

The two basic measurements are amplitude- and time-related and can be made using the sensitivity settings of the y amplitude and x timebase controls, assuming that both axes have been previously calibrated.

Signal amplitude peak-to-peak can be calculated from the product of total amplitude of the trace in cm and the y setting in V/cm. From this value the peak or RMS values can be calculated as required.

Similarly, the periodic time can be obtained from the product of the wavelength of one cycle in centimetres and the timebase setting in s/cm (or μs/cm or ms/cm accordingly). The reciprocal of this value of course provides the frequency of the waveform. The phase difference between two waveforms can be measured using a double-beam or dual-trace display. The wavelength λ of the primary trace is first obtained as above and then the distance d between corresponding points on the two waveforms can be measured. The phase difference is then calculated from $d(360/\lambda)°$. Strictly, this measurement is only applicable to sine-wave forms. For non-sinusoids, the time difference is more applicable.

Phase differences between two sine waves of the same frequency can also be measured using the technique of Lissajou's figures, which represents an application of the use of a nonlinear timebase. A series of such displays is shown in Figure 3.4. If two sine waves are input to x and y deflection systems and their amplitudes are carefully adjusted, the display will vary from a straight line, through a series of ellipses, to a circle in the manner indicated in Figure 3.4(a). Furthermore, this technique leads to the more complex displays shown in Figure 3.4(b), when the two waveforms are simple multiples of each other. In general, the ratio of the two frequencies here is given by:

$$\frac{f_y}{f_x} = \frac{\text{Number of loops horizontally}}{\text{Number of loops vertically}}$$

The Lissajou's figure technique can be extended to determine an unknown

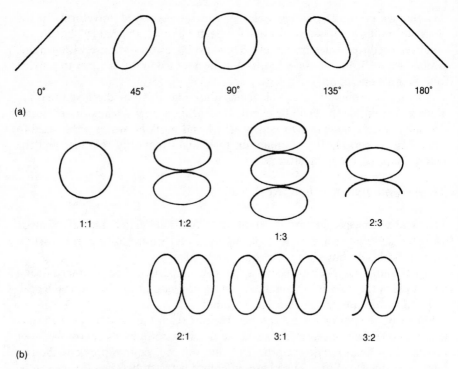

Figure 3.4 Lissajou's figures: (a) varying phase shift for $f_y/f_x = 1$; (b) varying ratios of f_y:f_x for a 90° phase shift

frequency. This is achieved by making a direct comparison of the unknown with the output from an accurately calibrated sine-wave signal generator.

Digital measurements

Processing a digital signal will create pulse distortion. What starts as a train of square pulses rapidly approachs sinusoids as the high-frequency components are progressively removed. Again, Lissajou's figures can be used to quantify this distortion. The basic principle is shown in Figure 3.5(a), where a digital data-stream is applied to the CRO y input. A sinusoidal timebase is provided at the external x input, running at a quarter of the bit rate. When the phasing of the two inputs is correctly adjusted, an *eye* pattern appears as indicated in Figure 3.5(b). The upper and lower levels of this trace, which represents the levels produced by a run of several consecutive 1s and 0s in the datastream, is taken as the maximum eye opening. The ratio of $a/b \times 100\%$ can therefore be used to evaluate the quality of the data signal at various points in the signal-processing chain.

Figure 3.5(c) shows the classical way in which an *eye height display* can be

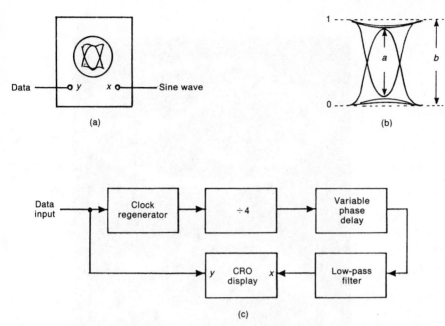

Figure 3.5 Eye diagrams

produced. The original datastream is used first to lock a local clock oscillator circuit to the bit rate. This is then divided by four and low-pass filtered to provide the one-quarter rate timebase frequency. The data and sinusoid are then input to the CRO as described above. An eye pattern will be displayed when the variable phase delay is correctly adjusted.

Figure 3.6 shows how this technique was used to evaluate the suitability of various magnetic tapes for digital recording. The results obtained with three cassettes are shown and the eye patterns represent the FSK data signals at a rate of 300 baud. The results clearly show the near 2:1 ratio of the bit frequencies, with the higher frequency producing the lower response. It is also clear that the high-quality audio tape provides a greater response for both 1s and 0s than either of the other two. When the test was repeated at a bit rate of 2400 baud, the results were even more convincing.

Storage oscilloscopes

Storage 'scopes are used to display fast one-shot, transient events or very low frequencies that change too slowly to be captured by the normal-persistence CRO tubes. These instruments are available in either digital or analogue form. In the digital form, the signal of interest is first captured, then digitized and stored in a semiconductor memory. From here it is readily available for future display and analysis. The analogue storage tube carries a fairly conventional

63

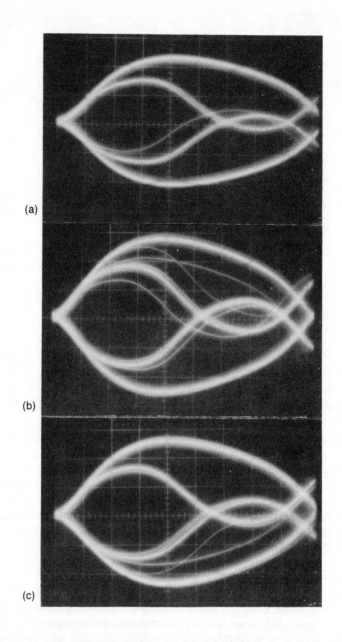

(a)

(b)

(c)

Figure 3.6   Eye diagrams (300 baud): (a) low-quality audio tape; (b) high-quality audio tape; (c) computer-grade tape

electron gun structure, but this *writes* an electron pattern on a mesh screen placed close to the tube face. Once it is captured, a second gun (the *flood gun*), unaffected by the deflection system, can be energized to flood the whole of the mesh area with electrons. This causes the pattern to be transferred to the tube face, where it is stored in the self-capacitance to be displayed until the gun potentials are equalized and the trace is erased.

Servicing CROs

This has much in common with television receiver servicing which was described in Volume 2 Part 2 of this series. However, by observation, faults may fairly easily be divided into three separate areas:

1 faults that affect the CRT and the power supplies;
2 faults associated with the timebase stages;
3 faults in the *y* amplifier stages that affect the work signal to be displayed.

Using the CRO

In order to utilize this versatile instrument to maximum advantage, especially its more sophisticated modes of operation, it is important to obtain as much practice as possible.

Function generators

Basically these are signal generators designed to produce sine, square or triangular waves as outputs. Each may be varied typically over a frequency range covering from less than 1 Hz to about 20 MHz. The basic frequency may be generated either by a highly stable oscillator circuit, or by using a frequency synthesizer. The output levels are typically variable between about 5 mV and 20 V peak of either polarity, plus a TTL-compatible signal at ±5 V. Some of the basic waveforms are shown in Figure 3.7. The output impedance is nominally 600 Ω and provision is made for driving signals via balanced or unbalanced lines.

Each of the basic output signals is capable of being modified. The sine wave may often be phase-shifted, and the square wave mark-to-space ratio is variable so that a pulse stream of variable-duty cycles can be provided. The triangular wave can be varied to provide a sawtooth of varying rise and fall periods. In addition, it is also possible to add a d.c. value to each output as an *offset*. This is valuable for testing circuits that are d.c.-coupled and with a frequency response that extends down to zero.

An additional feature often allows a second signal component to be gated

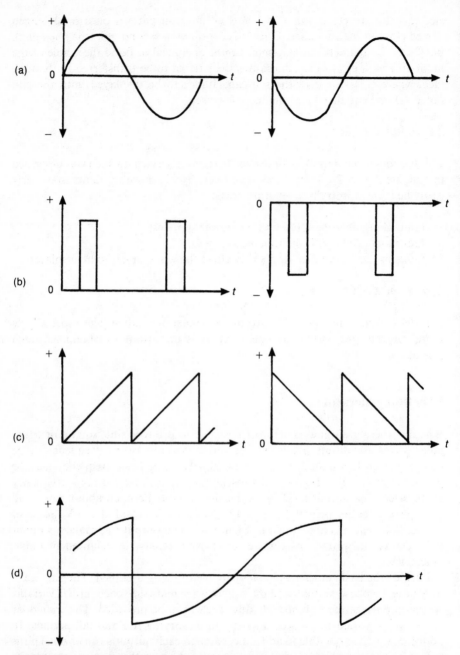

Figure 3.7 Function-generator waveforms: (a) sinusoidal; (b) positive and negative pulses; (c) positive and negative sawtooths (serrasoids); (d) compound wave

into the primary waveform in the manner indicated in Figure 3.7(d). A further variation of this is the *tone burst* that consists of a sine wave modulated with a parabolic envelope, but generated in bursts. This waveform is particularly suited to the testing of full-bandwidth audio systems or those circuits where strange resonances may occur. A variation of this feature utilizes a form of FM. Here, a basic sinusoid is frequency-swept between predetermined limits, either at a linear or logarithmic rate.

The more sophisticated instruments in this range may be equipped for microprocessor control, have a digital read-out of frequency and amplitude, plus a built-in standard frequency source.

Servicing problems

It is most important that the instrument calibration is carefully checked following any repairs. Service work is therefore a very specialized operation. Integrated circuits are extensively used, together with stabilized switched-mode power supplies. The highly critical oscillator circuit is invariably temperature-controlled.

Counter/timers

These devices, which range from simple hand-held models to complex laboratory bench instruments, are chiefly used for measuring signal frequency (or pulse-repetition frequency) over a range, typically from d.c. to more than 2 GHz.

The operation is based on pulse-counting over a known time period, from which the frequency is automatically determined. The read-out is usually presented on seven-segment LED or LCD displays. The principle of this technique was described in Volume 2 Part 1 of this series, to which the reader is referred for the basic information.

Counter/timers are often microprocessor-controlled with a basic clock frequency typically of 1 MHz. This is provided either by a *temperature-compensated crystal oscillator* (TCXO) or by an *oven-controlled crystal oscillator* (OCXO). Provision is often made for two-channel (A and B) measurements and these inputs may have different upper cut-off frequencies. Low-frequency noise can be troublesome with these instruments and so a low-pass filter with a cut-off frequency at about 10 kHz is often used at the inputs.

Facilities include absolute frequency, phase, period and time measurements, with frequency and time ratios for the A/B channels. Selectable gate times are used to extend the range of measurement. To extend the frequency range even further, a prescaler (a frequency divider $\div 10, \div 100$) can be connected between the source and the counter/timer.

67

Typical sensitivities range from about 20 mV at 5 Hz to about 150 mV at 150 MHz, with input impedances of the order of 1 MΩ in parallel with 40 pF. As for the CRO, × 10 probes are usually available for use with signals of an amplitude greater than the inbuilt attenuator can handle.

The resolution (the smallest change that can be registered) varies from about 0.1 Hz at the lower frequencies to 1 kHz at HF.

The more complex instruments in this range may be microprocessor-controlled. This allows for the inclusion of more elaborate features, such as hard-copy printouts and links to automatic test equipment (ATE) networks.

Servicing problems

Apart from power-supply problems, all the fault tracing will use digital techniques. Again, it is important that any service work should be concluded by recalibration. Therefore this form of work should only be entrusted to suitably equipped service departments.

Universal bridges

The basic Wheatstone bridge circuit that is used to determine the values of unknown resistances can be extended to evaluate unknown inductors and capacitors. In this case, the bridge must be energized from an a.c. source, the unknown device must be compared with a similar standard component, and the null detector must include a suitable a.c. rectifier circuit.

The basic a.c. bridge is shown in Figure 3.8(a) where it can be stated that the balance conditions occur when the products of opposite arms are equal. That is,

$$Z_1 Z_x = Z_2 Z_3$$

from which it can be deduced that the unknown

$$Z_x = \frac{Z_2 Z_3}{Z_1}$$

This simple concept, however, can only determine the component value and not evaluate its losses. In general, it is also necessary to determine the value of the equivalent series resistance of an inductor and the equivalent shunt resistance of a capacitor. In both cases, the resistive element represents the component losses which are related to its quality factor: the Q factor in the case of the inductor, and the loss angle (the angle by which the voltage/current relationship fails to reach the theoretical 90°) for the capacitor.

Figure 3.8(b) shows how the basic bridge concept can be extended to provide universal features. This bridge circuit may be energized either from an internal

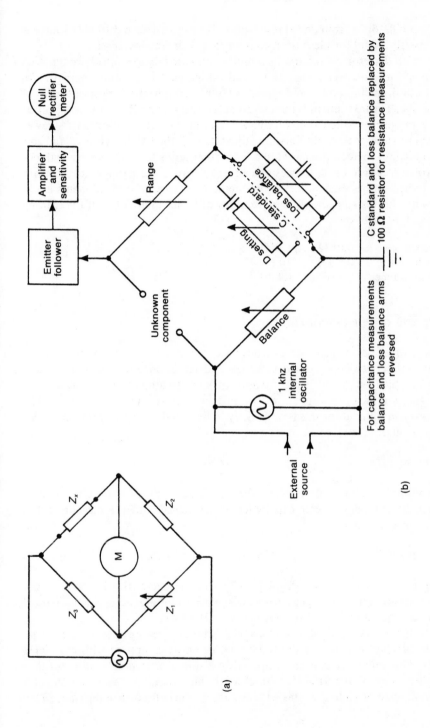

Figure 3.8 (a) General bridge circuit; (b) universal bridge (courtesy of Marconi Instruments Ltd)

1 kHz oscillator or from an external source. Using an external 10 kHz source is particularly useful for measuring components with very low losses.

The null detector circuit and its amplifier and sensitivity control are buffered by an emitter–follower circuit to minimize loading on the bridge network. In application, the unknown component is connected into the appropriate arm of the bridge. The instrument is then set to measure either an R, L or C component and a range is selected that provides a minimum meter deflection. A lower minimum value is then obtained by adjustment of the balance control and this then indicates the component value. By further adjustment of the loss balance control, a true zero meter indication can be achieved. The setting of this control then indicates the resistive loss component. The range of measurements available with this instrument, with an accuracy of better than $\pm 1\%$ of the reading obtained, is as follows:

resistance: $0.01\ \Omega$ to $11\ \text{M}\Omega$
inductance: $0.2\ \mu\text{H}$ to $110\ \text{H}$
capacitance: $0.5\ \text{pF}$ to $1100\ \mu\text{F}$

Servicing of universal bridges

Certain of these instruments are designed for portable field work and are therefore likely to be subjected to shock and vibration. Local service work is therefore likely to involve the ravages of such treatment. Since the overall accuracy is critical, any repair work must be followed by recalibration. The necessary equipment for this is only likely to be found in specially set-up service departments.

Exercise 3.1

With a function generator providing the input signals, practise using an oscilloscope in all its modes, to gain experience of this device both as a measuring and display instrument.

Exercise 3.2

Using the internal test waveform provided in the CRO (this is commonly a 50 Hz square wave, 1 V peak-to-peak signal), calibrate both the y channel amplifier, the timebase and the associated $\times 10$ probe.

As a further exercise, calibrate this internal test signal against some external standard. The frequency of the square wave can be compared with the 50 Hz mains. The amplitude can be compared by using a *Standard Weston cell* that provides an e.m.f. of 1.0186 V at 20 °C. With the y attenuator set to 1 V/cm and the input selector set to d.c., this will produce a 1 cm deflection in the trace. Both

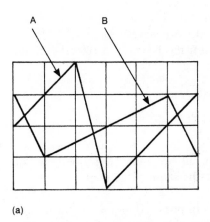

(a)

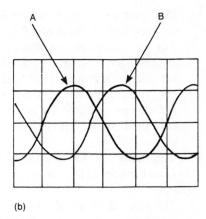

(b)

Figure 3.9   CRT waveform traces (graticule represents 1 cm squares)

calibrations will be to an accuracy of about 1%. (If a standard cell is not available, a new 1.5 V mercury dry cell can be used — but producing 1.5 cm deflection — with a reasonable degree of accuracy.)

Exercise 3.3

Using a universal bridge, compare the values obtained for a number of R, L and C components each with nominally the same values. In particular, inductors and capacitors can show a marked difference in loss values. It can also be useful to measure the self-inductance of some wire-wound resistors.

Exercise 3.4

Using the output of a function generator, together with a suitable instrument to measure the signal amplitude, experiment with various chart and pen recorders to evaluate their cut-off frequencies (-3 dB) and input sensitivities.

Test questions

1   The y channel amplifier of an oscilloscope has just been repaired. Describe the next step necessary before the instrument is again used for service. Describe a simple way in which the y amplifier bandwidth can be ascertained.

2   For the waveforms in Figure 3.9(a), the y attenuator has been set to 4 V/cm and the timebase x to 100 ms/cm. Evaluate:
   (a)   the peak-to-peak amplitudes of waveforms A and B;

71

(b) the time period by which B leads A;

(c) the periodic time and frequency of the two waveforms.

For the waveforms in (b), the y attenuator has been set to 100 mV/cm and the timebase x to 100 μs/cm. Evaluate:

(a) the peak amplitude of both waveforms;

(b) the time period by which A leads B;

(c) the phase difference between A and B;

(d) the frequency of both waveforms.

3 The stepper motor in a control system fails to rotate. Describe how you would use suitable instruments to locate the cause of the fault.

4 The phase detector of a system requires in-phase (I) and a quadrature (Q) signals at a frequency of 500 kHz for accurate demodulation. Describe a method of adjusting this pair of signals to ensure the necessary 90° of phase difference.

5 Give three examples where it may be necessary to provide a permanent record of system output parameters. List the most suitable recording instruments in each case.

6 A magnetic cassette recorder is being used to record the output data of a system. Describe the problems that might arise if a fault in the tape capstan circuit causes the motor speed to fluctuate.

4 Transducers and sensors

Summary

Principles, characteristics and applications of transducers and sensors for electrical/electronic controlled systems. Transducers, sensors and circuits for specific applications. (Syllabus section 7.4)

Introduction

As explained in Chapter 1, sensors and transducers perform similar functions. Essentially, both are used to generate an electrical signal from the controlled variable being measured. Although many control systems function in a completely mechanical manner, electrical/electronic controllers have a number of significant advantages, because the signals:

1 can be transmitted over much greater distances;
2 can easily be processed, amplified and filtered;
3 can easily be subjected to mathematical functions such as differentiation (rate of change) and integration, and can be scanned for limiting values.

Most practical systems will include some form of signal-conditioning circuit. This acts as an interface to ensure compatibility between the output from the sensor/transducer and the input to the controller. Signal conditioning precedes requirements for amplification, linearization or frequency compensation, filtering and, in the case of digital controllers, analogue-to-digital conversion. The Wheatstone bridge plus buffer amplifier forms a popular signal conditioner. Systems that have a long feedback path from the transducer/sensor tend to suffer from attenuation and noise. Also, with d.c. signals, it is often difficult to distinguish between the wanted signal and spurious signals caused by time and temperature drift. These problems can be overcome by using a modulated carrier for the feedback signal. In particular, the use of FM is most effective in suppressing noise signals.

From the above, it is clear that this section of the control system may well consist of several electronic elements in series. The overall *sensitivity* then becomes the product of the individual sensitivities as follows:

Transducer sensitivity = 0.4 mV/°C
Amplifier gain = 1000 (1 V/mV)
Recorder sensitivity = 10 mm/V

The overall sensitivity is thus:

$$\frac{0.4 \text{ mV} \times 1 \text{ V} \times 10 \text{ mm}}{°C \times mV \times V} = 4 \text{ mm/°C}$$

By comparison, the element accuracies combine to form a geometric average as indicated by the following example:

Transducer accuracy = ±4%
Amplifier accuracy = ±3%
Recorder accuracy = ±5%

The overall accuracy will be given by

$$\pm \sqrt{(4^2 + 3^2 + 5^2)} = \pm 7.07\%$$

Transducers fall into one of two basic classes: passive or active. Passive transducers require the application of an external energizing e.m.f. and active transducers are simply self-generating. *Passive* transducers include resistive, capacitive, inductive and mutual inductive devices; active types include electromagnetic, thermoelectric, photoemissive and piezoelectric devices.

The important general transducer characteristics include the following:

Resolution: The smallest input change that the device can respond to: usually measured as a percentage of the full scale range.
Range: The total spread of input values that the device is capable of responding to.
Bandwidth: Since most devices need to have a d.c. response, the bandwidth is equal to the upper cut-off (−3 dB) frequency.

Response time: This is usually stated as the time taken for the device output to rise to some specified percentage of its full scale range, in response to a step change at the input.

Servicing sensors and transducers

These are normally very robust devices with a long working lifetime. Owing to the nature of their construction, many are not repairable. Servicing therefore involves testing to locate the cause of a fault followed by replacement and possible recalibration of the system. In general, testing involves using one of two techniques. For active devices the generated e.m.f. needs to be measured under operating conditions, using a meter with a high input impedance. The current flowing through passive devices will usually need to be obtained indirectly. It can be derived by measuring the voltage developed across a series resistor in the circuit and then using Ohm's law to calculate the current flowing. If a suitable resistor is not already fitted to the circuit, a 10 Ω close-tolerance component can be added temporarily, when every millivolt measured represents 100 μA of current. The main difficulty lies in choosing a suitable instrument that does not load the transducer output impedance and distort the measured values.

Photoelectric transducers

As the title suggests, these devices convert light energy into electrical signals. They are used extensively in position sensing and counting devices where the interruption of a light beam is converted into an electrical signal. As most of these devices have a wavelength response greater than the human eye, their applications extend into the infrared region. Figure 4.1 shows the typical human-eye response in relationship to the infrared wavelengths.

The intensity of device illumination may be quoted in one of two ways: in units of *lux* (lx) that represent the illumination per unit area, or in the more familiar terms of mW/cm^2 when it is described as the *irradiance*. There is no direct conversion between these units unless other quantities such as the spectral composition of the light are maintained constant: then for the range of values usually associated with photoelectric devices, a useful approximation is given by 1 mW/cm^2 = 200 lx.

Useful simple tests for serviceability can be made by studying the variation of the device output signal between conditions of exposure to normal light levels and when capped.

Photoconductive cells

The resistance of certain materials decreases when subjected to increased illumination. The common materials used for light-dependent resistors (LDRs) as

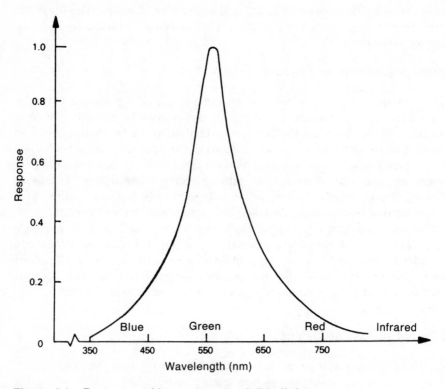

Figure 4.1   Response of human eye to visible light

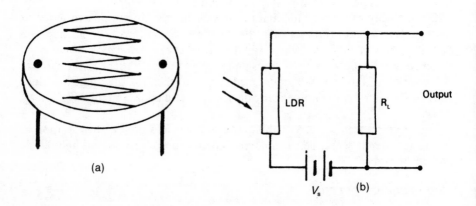

Figure 4.2   (a) The photoconductive cell; (b) basic circuit

these devices are called include selenium, cadmium sulphide, cadmium selenide and lead sulphide. Each material responds to different wavelengths of light. Figure 4.2(a) shows the general appearance of a photoconductive cell and its construction. Gold-conducting sections are deposited on a glass plate with a long, meandering gap to isolate the two sections. A thin layer of suitable photoconductive material is then deposited to bridge the insulating region. This construction is necessary to reduce the cell's resistance to a usable value. Typical resistance values for various cells range from about 500 kΩ to 10 MΩ in darkness and from about 1 kΩ to 100 kΩ in bright light. The change in resistance is nonlinear and there is a significant time lag of up to 0.1 s in response to a pulse of light. Figure 4.2(b) shows a basic circuit using a LDR. The current flowing in the load resistance R_L due to the supply voltage V_s produces the output voltage. Increasing the illumination of the LDR lowers its resistance so that the current, and hence the output voltage, increases. The maximum permitted voltage for these cells may be as high as 300 V and the maximum power dissipation is in the order of 300 mW. The dark-to-light resistance ratio ranges from about 50:1 to 250:1. The cells are particularly sensitive to red light and the infrared wavelengths, so that they are often used as flame detectors in boiler and furnace control systems.

As indicated by the characteristic of a typical photoconductive cell shown in Figure 4.3, the greatest nonlinearity occurs at higher illumination levels.

Photodiodes

Photodiodes (Figure 4.4) are formed with one very thin junction region and equipped with a lens so that light energy can be directed into the depletion region. When this happens 'hole–electron' pairs are generated to increase the diode's conductivity. Such diodes have a peak response in the infrared region, but the response to visible light is still very useful. The diodes are operated either reverse-biased, or very lightly forward-biased (to increase sensitivity) so that no current flows. Typical 'dark current' is as low as 2 nA, rising to about 100 μA in bright light for germanium types. Modern PIN silicon versions may have a peak power dissipation greater than 100 mW. The increase in current due to the light is practically linear. The response time to a pulse of light is very short so that they find applications in high-speed switching circuits. Generally, the small output and high impedance are disadvantages and so a buffer amplifier is usually needed.

The basic circuit configuration is shown in Figure 4.5 whilst the more practical application of a light meter is shown in Figure 4.6. With both diodes shielded from light, the conduction of the two transistors forming part of the bridge circuit is balanced by resistor R so that there is no current flowing through the meter. In operation D_2 is maintained in darkness and the base voltage of Tr_1 and hence its collector current depends on the level of light falling on D_1.

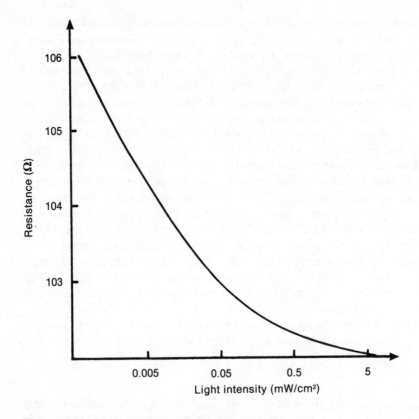

Figure 4.3   Characteristic of photoconductive cell

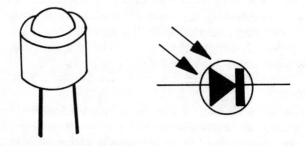

Figure 4.4   Photodiode and circuit symbol

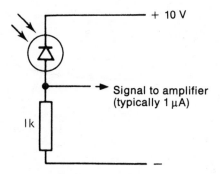

Figure 4.5   A silicon photodiode (input circuit)

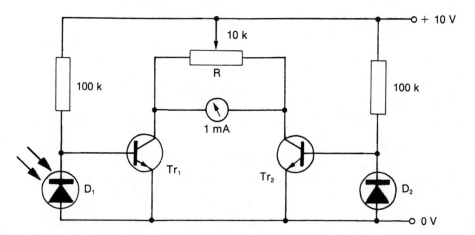

Figure 4.6   Circuit of light meter

An increase in the illumination of D_1 causes Tr_1 collector current to decrease, its collector voltage rises and so the meter deflects from its zero position.

Phototransistors

A phototransistor has a similar construction to a silicon planar transistor except that it is equipped with a lens so that light can be made to shine directly into the base–emitter junction. It also has similar V/I characteristics to the common-emitter amplifier as indicated by Figure 4.7. The response time to a pulse of light is in the order of 1–2 μs and phototransistors are therefore mostly used in medium-speed light detector circuits. The current ranges from about 25–50 μA in darkness to about 5–10 mA in bright light. The phototransistor is connected so that the base is either open-circuit, reverse-biased, or only very slightly

79

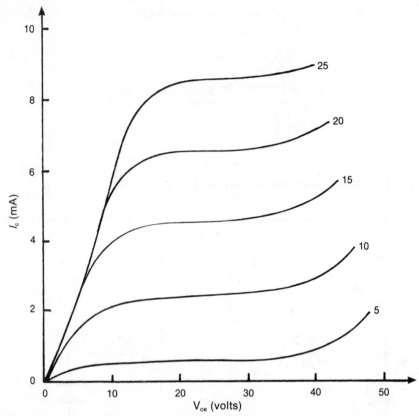

Figure 4.7   Phototransistor characteristic (for increasing irradiance mW/cm²)

forward-biased. In some devices, the base connection is omitted altogether so that only the collector and emitter connections can be used. The load may be placed in either the collector or emitter leads as shown in Figure 4.8. Light shining into the base–emitter junction modulates the base current which is in turn magnified by the current gain. Such a device can be used to drive a load directly as shown in Figure 4.9.

Light-emitting diodes (LEDs)

The operation of the photodiode was shown to be dependent upon the application of energy to generate hole–electron pairs. Conversely, when holes and electrons recombine, energy is released. In germanium and silicon, this energy is released as heat into the crystal structure. However, in materials such as gallium arsenide and gallium phosphide this energy is released as light, different semiconductor compounds releasing light of different wavelengths. The basic struc-

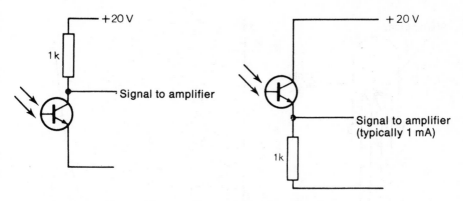

Figure 4.8   A phototransistor as a light-level detector

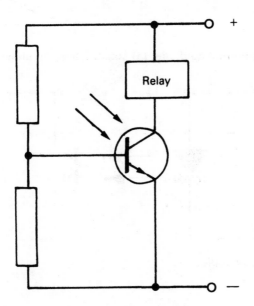

Figure 4.9   A phototransistor as a relay driver

ture of the diode is shown in Figure 4.10(a). The plastic moulding not only holds the component parts together but also acts as a light-pipe so that most of the light generated is radiated from the domed region. A characteristic typical of a light-emitting diode is shown in Figure 4.10(b). When forward-biased beyond about 1.6 V, the current rises rapidly and light is radiated from the junction. The current should be limited to a value less than about 40 mA by the use of a series resistor.

81

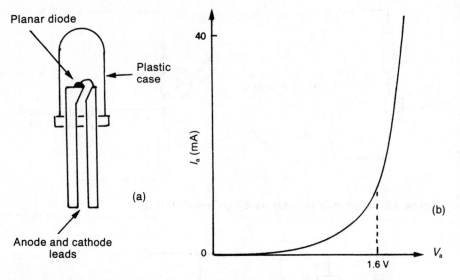

Figure 4.10   Light-emitting diode: (a) construction; (b) characteristic

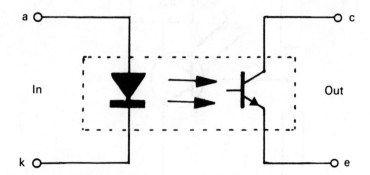

Figure 4.11   Opto-coupler

Opto-couplers

These consist of an LED and phototransistor pair as shown in Figure 4.11. The input signal modulates the diode current and hence the intensity of its light output. This variation in light produces a variation in collector current to provide an output signal. Since the light beam has no electrical impedance, there is no matching problem between input and output circuits. The electrical isolation is very high and an opto-coupler can withstand test voltages as high as 4 kV between input and output terminals. Alternatively the LED can be used to launch energy into a glass optical fibre cable to transmit the signal over very much greater distances. The light path within the opto-coupler can be interrupted by a shutter. This generates a pulsating signal that might be used to drive a counter circuit capable of working at high speed.

The phototransistor may be replaced by a compound transistor (Darlington amplifier) to provide higher gain, or by a photothyristor to provide higher output current. However, both arrangements result in a lower switching speed.

Shaft encoders (also known as digital resolvers)

These devices use the opto-coupler principle to generate a digital signal due to rotation, directly and without a separate analogue-to-digital converter. They consist of a small circular grating attached to an input spindle. Infrared light generated by an LED shines through the disc and on to a photodetector. As the disc rotates, the grating interrupts the light beam to generate a digital bit stream. Often a second opto-coupler is added and this provides an output that is phase-shifted relative to the first beam. The addition of a simple logic circuit then provides a means of detecting the direction of rotation.

Two types of encoder are available, described as *incremental* or *absolute* devices. The incremental device provides a serial bitstream output during rotation and requires the addition of a counter circuit. Unlike the incremental encoder, where the disc grating is basically a series of peripheral slits, the absolute encoder disc is equipped with a number of concentric tracks that carry alternate transparent and opaque sectors. These tracks each form one of the parallel bit patterns that provide the output signal. These discs are often described as being Gray-coded because the bit patterns change in a manner similar to the following 16 four-bit code patterns:

Gray code	Binary code	Gray code	Binary code
0000	0000	1100	1000
0001	0001	1101	1001
0011	0010	1111	1010
0010	0011	1110	1011
0110	0100	1010	1100
0111	0101	1011	1101
0101	0110	1001	1110
0100	0111	1000	1111

The Gray code system is used because there is only one bit change between values. This limits the errors due to noise and in particular limits the error to just one bit if the shaft stops exactly between two code positions.

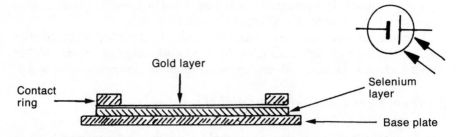

Figure 4.12 Section through photovoltaic cell, and its circuit symbol

Photovoltaic devices

A layer of selenium is deposited on an iron or aluminium backing plate which forms the positive pole. A transparent layer of gold is evaporated on to this to form the negative pole. A metallic contact ring completes the circuit. The general construction and circuit symbol are shown in Figure 4.12. Light shines through the gold film into the layer of selenium. This releases electrons that form an electric field within the selenium, making the gold layer the negative pole of the cell. The whole cell is enclosed in a plastic housing with a transparent window for protection. The maximum current in bright light depends on the particular cell, but short-circuit currents in excess of 1 mA can be obtained. Such cells are suitable to drive a portable photographic light meter. Figure 4.13 shows how excessive loading can reduce the output voltage of these cells. Modern lightmeters use silicon photovoltaic junction devices which have a more suitable spectral response.

Solar cells

These are the semiconductor version of the selenium cell. They are formed from heavily doped *p–n* junctions. A cell of about 4 cm² is capable of providing 0.6 V on open circuit, with a short-circuit current of up to 100 mA in bright light.

Such cells may be linked together in a series/parallel configuration to provide much higher levels of power supply. The large *wings* of communications satellites form a good example of this technique.

Thermistors

These devices may be in rod, bead, washer or disc form. They are made from carefully controlled mixtures of certain metallic oxides, sintered at very high temperatures to produce a ceramic finish. Thermistors have a large *temperature coefficient of resistance* given by the expression

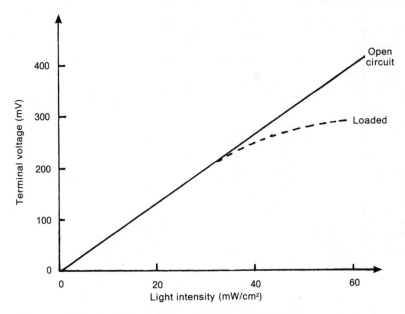

Figure 4.13 Photovoltaic cell output versus illumination

$$\frac{\text{Change of resistance}}{\text{Original resistance} \times \text{Change of temperature}}$$

In normal resistors, this value is relatively small and positive, typically in the order of 3×10^{-3}. For thermistors however, the temperature coefficient can be of the order of 15 to 50×10^{-3}. Negative temperature coefficient (NTC) thermistors have resistances that fall with a rise in temperature and are commonly made from mixtures of the oxides of manganese, cobalt, copper and nickel. Positive temperature coefficient (PTC) components whose resistance increases with a rise in temperature can be made from barium titanate with carefully controlled amounts of lead or strontium. A typical characteristic is shown in Figure 4.14.

Thermistors are used extensively for temperature measurement and control up to about 400 °C. A typical circuit is shown in Figure 4.15 where the bridge circuit is balanced at some low temperature so that the output from the differential amplifier is zero. Th_2 is maintained at this low temperature, while Th_1 is exposed to the temperature to be measured. A rise in the temperature of Th_1 causes its resistance to rise and lower the voltage at one of the amplifier inputs. The amplifier output now changes in proportion to the rise in temperature. The addition of a thermistor to the bias network of an amplifier can be used to stabilize it against the effects of temperature change. Another application is to provide temperature compensation for the change in the winding resistance of alternators and other generators which affects their performance when the operating temperature rises.

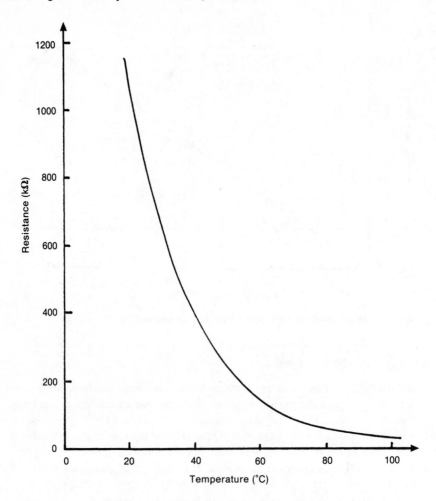

Figure 4.14   Thermistor characteristic

Note the use of the symbol t° alongside the PTC thermistors in Figure 4.15. Had Th_1 and Th_2 been NTC devices the symbol $-t°$ would have been used.

Thermocouples

When two dissimilar metals are in contact with each other a *contact potential* is developed between them. This is known as the *Seebeck* or *thermoelectric* effect. The voltage, which rises with temperature, is almost linear over several hundred degrees. If two junctions are formed as shown in Figure 4.16(a), a current will flow around the circuit provided that each junction is at a different temperature.

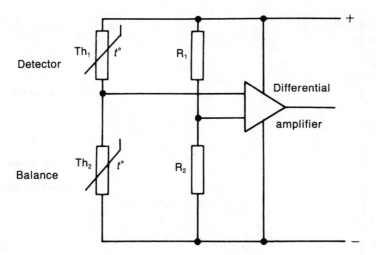

Figure 4.15   A thermistor bridge

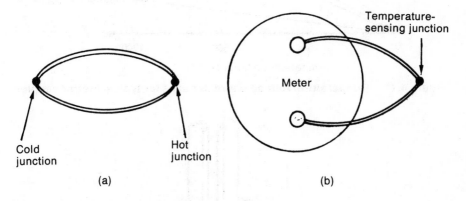

Figure 4.16   The principle of the thermocouple

The circuit can be modified as shown in Figure 4.16(b) to include a meter which now becomes one of the junctions, the other becoming the temperature sensor. By reversing the meter connections, temperatures below ambient can be measured. The two metals are chosen to maximize the contact potential for a particular temperature range. The metals used include:

iron and copper–nickel alloy;
copper and copper–nickel alloy;
nickel–chromium alloy and copper–nickel alloy;
nickel–chromium alloy and nickel–aluminium–manganese alloy.

The characteristics of a number of popular thermocouple materials are shown

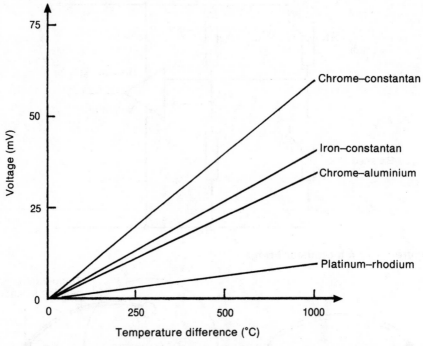

Figure 4.17   Temperature/voltage characteristics for typical thermocouples

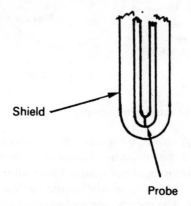

Figure 4.18   A typical high-temperature probe

in Figure 4.17. These allow for a range of instruments to measure temperatures from − 85 °C up to 2000 °C. For most temperature measurements, the hot junction is formed into a probe as shown in Figure 4.18. The metal sheath is used to protect the junction from environmental hazards and is electrically

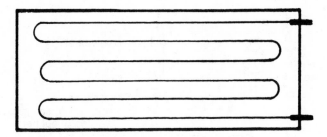

Figure 4.19   A resistance strain gauge

isolated from it with magnesium oxide. This material has good thermal conductivity with high electrical resistance (up to 1000 MΩ).

Resistance strain gauge

When a body is under stress, it undergoes a proportional change in its dimensions. This proportional change is referred to as *strain*. When electrical conductors are stressed, the resultant strain causes a variation of their resistance. A resistance strain gauge consists of a long, fine wire folded to fit on a small area as shown in Figure 4.19 and fixed to a flexible backing. If the gauge is now firmly fixed with an epoxy adhesive to part of a structure such as a tower, pylon, bridge, or building, any relative movement of parts of the structure will cause a change in the dimensions of the gauge and hence vary its resistance. The gauge factor is defined as

$$\frac{\text{Percentage change of resistance}}{\text{Percentage change of strain}}$$

which is typically in the order of 2 for metallic wire gauges. This small change of resistance constitutes the output signal. A modern strain gauge is made by a method similar to printed circuits. A metal foil is deposited on a flexible insulator and the metal is photo-etched away to provide a very fine grid pattern. This type is usually known as a *foil strain gauge*. It has the advantage of being thinner and more flexible and hence more sensitive to small magnitudes of strain.

Strain gauges are generally used in conjunction with a bridge circuit with gauges being connected into two arms of the bridge in the manner shown in Figure 4.20. One gauge is fastened to the structure it is protecting, while the other is left free of mechanical strain (the *dummy* gauge). The purpose of this arrangement is that, since strain gauge signals are of very small amplitude (only a few microvolts d.c.), a change in the ambient temperature could easily produce in a single (fastened) gauge unwanted signals that would swamp a

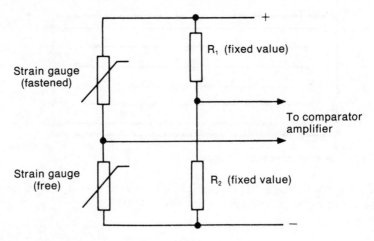

Figure 4.20 Strain gauges in a bridge circuit

danger signal possibly being given by the gauge at the same time. The arrangement described ensures that, since temperature changes now affect both gauges equally, the balance of the bridge is left unimpaired. If a change of strain now occurs, it affects *only* the gauge which is mechanically fastened to the structure it is protecting. The electrical balance of the bridge is altered by a *wanted* signal only, and a valid reading can be obtained.

In many cases, such a bridge circuit would be a.c.-energized, to enable the small output to be more easily amplified.

Semiconductor strain gauge

In crystalline materials such as germanium and silicon the pressure-resistive (piezoresistive) effect is quite large, typically in the order of 200 times that of the resistive strain gauge. To offset this advantage, the semiconductor strain gauge has a high temperature coefficient of resistance. In practice, this temperature dependence is overcome by producing a gauge with two devices in series, each having practically equal but opposite temperature coefficients, and by the bridge connection, noted above.

Resistance potentiometer

Resistance potentiometers ('pots') transducers are basically variable resistances as shown schematically in Figure 4.21(a) and (b). Variation of slider position produces a variation in the output voltage V_{out} (Figure 4.22). In a practical arrangement, the potentiometer may be one element of a bridge circuit. The

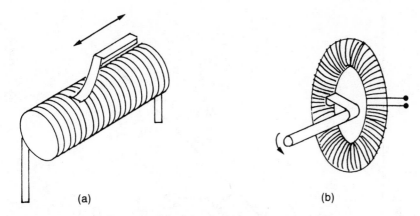

Figure 4.21   Resistive potentiometer: (a) linear; (b) rotary

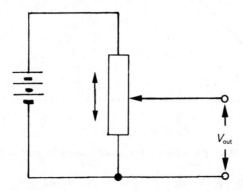

Figure 4.22   Resistance potentiometer with d.c. supply

supply voltage may be d.c. as shown in Figure 4.22 or, as is more common, driven from an a.c. source. This latter method makes any amplification needed more simple. The disadvantage of the potentiometer is that the linearity of the system is dependent upon the value of load resistance into which the device has to work.

Figure 4.23 illustrates this loading effect and the error that arises. Unless the potentiometer is loaded with a high impedance, the output is only accurate at the resistance ends, with maximum error occurring at about 50% displacement. Such a transducer therefore requires the use of a buffer amplifier.

The single-turn rotary unit is restricted to a range of about 330° of arc. An extended range is provided by the 'ten-turn pot', where the resistance coil is formed into a ten-turn spiral. Such a device has a range of almost 3600°.

Unless the pot is of the slide wire type, the resolution is controlled by the individual turns of resistance wire. (The slide wire has an infinitely small

91

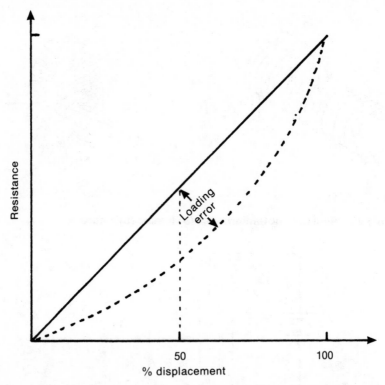

Figure 4.23   Resistive potentiometer characteristic and loading effect

resolution.) Because of the abrasive nature of the sliding contact, these transducers are prone to generating contact noise.

Capacitive transducer

The capacitance of a parallel plate capacitor is given by

$$C = \frac{\varepsilon A}{d}$$

where ε is the dielectric permittivity, A is the effective area of overlap of the plates and d is the distance between them. The variation of either A or ε produces a linear transducer. The general principle is shown in Figure 4.24. The change of capacitance per unit displacement in either direction is small, typically in the order of a few tens of picofarads.

Figure 4.25 shows the effects of these variables and the way small changes of d also produce practically linear results. The diagram also shows the greater degree of sensitivity obtained in region a relative to that in b.

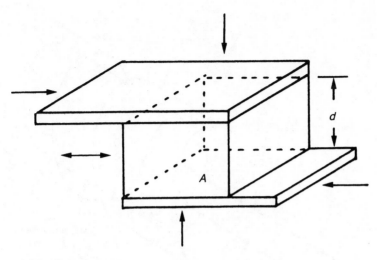

Figure 4.24 Principle of capacitive transducer showing degrees of movement

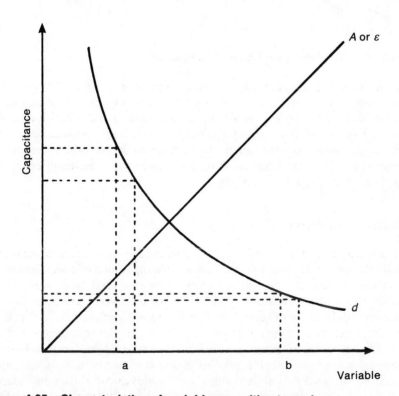

Figure 4.25 Characteristics of variable capacitive transducer

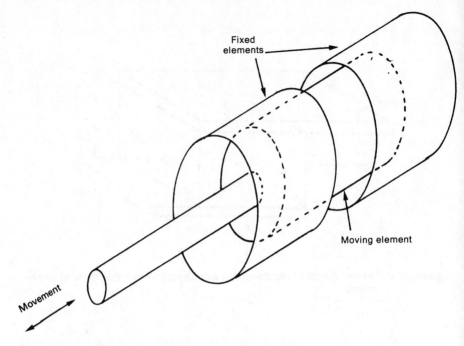

Figure 4.26   Differential capacitive transducer

A convenient way of using this device is to couple it to an oscillator's tuned circuit, where displacement of the transducer produces a change of frequency. This can be measured on a frequency meter or counter. An alternative version is shown in Figure 4.26: the differential capacitive transducer. Displacement of the central core causes one capacitance to increase while the other decreases. If connected to a bridge circuit as shown in Figure 4.27, the small change of capacitance becomes more significant.

Inductive transducer

There are many variants of the inductive transducer, but most are based on the transformer principle, where an a.c. current flowing in one winding induces an a.c. voltage in another. One of the most commonly used types is the linear variable differential transformer (LVDT), whose basic principle can be explained with the aid of Figure 4.28. The a.c. input signal, usually in the 50 Hz to 10 kHz frequency range, induces two voltages in the secondary windings which are connected in series opposition. The output signal is therefore the difference between the two voltages. With the core in the central position, equal voltages are induced so that the output is zero. Movement of the core in either direction results in one voltage increasing and the other decreasing. Thus

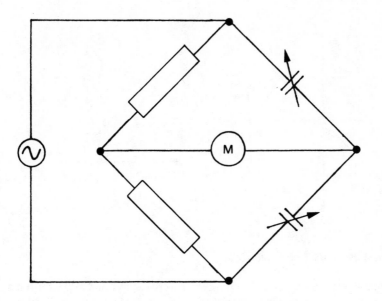

Figure 4.27   Circuit application of capacitive transducer

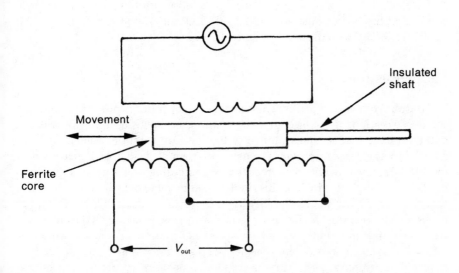

Figure 4.28   The linear variable differential transformer (LVDT)

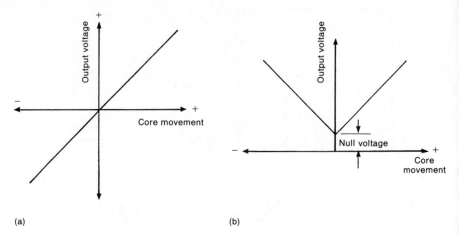

(a)   (b)

Figure 4.29   LVDT characteristic

displacement of the core causes an increase in the amplitude of the output signal, so that an a.c. meter connected to the transformer will give an indication of the magnitude of core movement but not its direction. For equal amplitudes of displacement in opposite directions the output voltage will have opposite phase displacements. Therefore to obtain an indication of magnitude and direction of displacement, the LVDT has to be connected to a phase-sensitive detector.

This theoretical characteristic is shown in Figure 4.29(a). However, in a practical circuit, even with the core in its central position, stray effects will ensure that the two voltages are not exactly 180° out of phase. This results in a small *null voltage* as indicated in Figure 4.29(b).

Tachogenerator

The output voltage of a permanent magnet d.c. generator is proportional to the speed of rotation. If coupled to some rotating mechanism, it will provide an output voltage that is representative of the speed of rotation. Such a device is referred to as a *tachogenerator*. The main problem of the d.c. tachogenerator is the high-frequency ripple generated by commutation which is superimposed upon the d.c. output. Much of this ripple could be removed with filters, but this sometimes leads to system instability. An a.c. version is also available, known as the *drag-cup* generator. A simple a.c. generator would generate an output whose frequency and amplitude depend on speed of rotation and hence would be difficult to use in a servo system. The drag-cup generator shown schematically in Figure 4.30 overcomes the varying-frequency problem to provide an output voltage proportional to rotational speed only. The conducting sleeve, of copper or aluminium, is coupled to the rotating mechanism. The output signal fre-

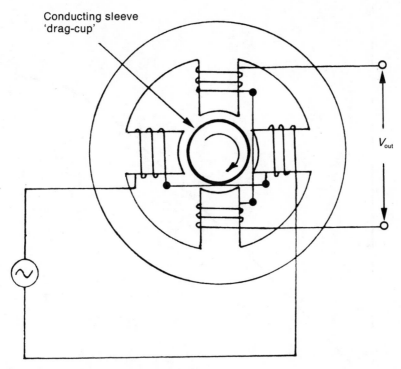

Conducting sleeve
'drag-cup'

V_{out}

Figure 4.30   The a.c. tachogenerator

quency is controlled from the a.c. input but the output amplitude depends on the speed of the drag-cup.

Figure 4.31 shows the characteristic for a small d.c. tachogenerator, together with the saturation effect that occurs at higher speed. A feature of the d.c. device, that is sometimes useful, is that it generates an output voltage of the opposite polarity when driven in reverse.

Measurements

Physical quantities are measured using the Système International (SI) of units which is based on seven fundamental units:

mass (kilogram, kg);
length (metre, m);
time (second, s);
electric current (ampere, A);
thermodynamic temperature (kelvin, K);
luminous intensity (candela, cd);
amount of substance (mole, mol).

97

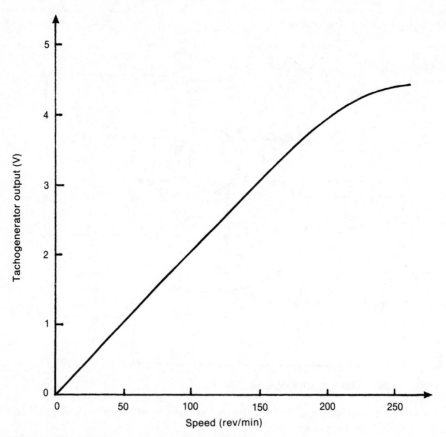

Figure 4.31 Tachogenerator characteristic

All the other neccessary units can be derived from this basic set. Mass is simply the amount of matter contained in a body, but is more precisely defined as the ratio of the force F that when applied to a body produces acceleration a. Thus mass $m = F/a$, and within terrestrial constraints, m is constant. If a braking force is applied to a moving body, it may cause deceleration, equivalent to a negative acceleration.

However, not all motions of interest will be linear; in many cases, circular or rotary motion needs to be measured. From Figure 4.32 it can be shown that any radius that rotates in a smooth and continuous manner will trace out amplitude variations that represent a sine wave.

Angular velocity $=$ angle/time ($°$/s)
Frequency f (Hz) $=$ number of revolutions per second (rev/s)
Time for one revolution (s) $= 1/f$ (the periodic time t)

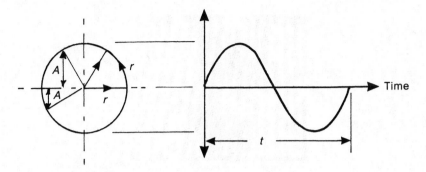

Figure 4.32   Angular velocity and the sine wave

Angles may also be measured in radians, which can be explained by reference to Figure 4.32. If the radius r sweeps through a circumferential distance also of r, then the angle swept out is described as 1 radian (rad). Since the circumference of the circle $= 2\pi r$, then there will be 2π radians per 360°. The angular velocity ω rad/s of the rotating radius is then given by

$$\frac{2\pi}{t} = \frac{2\pi}{1/f} = 2\pi f \, \text{rad/s}$$

Pure measurement systems have much in common with open-loop control systems, except that the transducer or sensor is used to obtain a signal that is representative of some specific measurement.

Measurement of length, displacement or position

These three quantities are all related to distance measurements. While length is usually considered to be a scalar quantity, there are times when direction must also be considered; this quantity then acquires vector or phasor properties. Displacement is simply the distance moved by a body from one point to another. The term *position* implies that some form of memory is needed to recognize where the body has moved to in relationship to its resting place at some previous point in time.

Linear displacement may be measured using either a *linear-resistive potentiometer* (LVDT), or capacitive transducers, or more elegantly using an electro-optical method based on the interference patterns generated by two diffraction gratings. The principle is shown in Figure 4.33. With this method, measurement of lengths from a few microns (10^{-6} metres) to several metres is possible. As the moving grating passes over the fixed one the interference pattern will appear to

Figure 4.33 Measurement of length using diffraction grating method

move up or down depending on the direction of relative movement. By placing the gratings within an opto-coupler, the moving pattern will generate pulses of current. The distance moved can be evaluated from a knowledge of the dimensions of the gratings and the number of pulses generated. Alternatively, the use of a counter/timer will allow the linear velocity to be measured.

This concept can be extended to measure lengths to a very high degree of accuracy using laser light. The basic principles of laser interferometry can be explained by reference to Figure 4.34, where light from the laser source is split into two paths using glass plates. The object whose displacement is to be measured provides reflected light that travels over path 2. When the deflected light (path 2) and the direct rays (path 1) impinge upon the screen, the light energies add according to the phase relationship produced by the differing path lengths. When two waves of the same frequency interact, they produce interference or Moiré patterns. The addition of two in-phase waves produces a larger wave and this is described as constructive interference. By comparison, two anti-phase waves produce a very small resultant and destructive interference.

The overall effect of the interference is that banding occurs on the screen as shown in Figure 4.34. When used in the manner shown, a movement of the object by half a wavelength causes the banding pattern to move a distance equal to one wavelength of the laser light. As a typical example using laser interferometry, it is possible to measure with a resolution of $\lambda/2 = 0.33$ µm, and to an accuracy of 1.5 ppm (parts per million) or 0.0015 µm/mm.

Digital measuring systems

It is possible to use rack-and-pinion gearing to couple a shaft encoder to the linear measuring system. In this case, the absolute type of encoder is often preferred because it produces a direct digital output value without the need for a separate counter circuit.

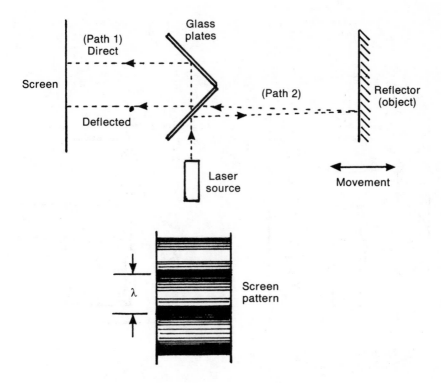

Figure 4.34   Measurement by laser interferometry

Force

Force is defined as that which causes a body to change its state of motion, or its shape. In SI units, the force F in newtons is given by the product of mass m in kg and acceleration a in m/s², i.e. $F = ma$. If the only component of acceleration is that due to gravity, then a can be considered to be constant and F is proportional to m. Therefore for earthbound measurements F can usually be found by *weighing*.

A *load cell*, whose basic construction is shown in Figure 4.35(a), is often used for measuring forces ranging from less than 5 kg to more than 5×10^6 kg. Four strain gauges are mounted on an elastic member as shown, and when an axial load is applied, the compressive force reduces the length of gauges G_2 and G_4, lowering their resistance. Since the volume of the member remains constant, it spreads diametrically to introduce forces that increase the tensions in gauges G_1 and G_3, thus increasing their resistance. Since the gauges are wired in a bridge configuration as indicated by Figure 4.35(b), the unbalance output voltage that is produced will be proportional to the distortion and hence to the load. Because

101

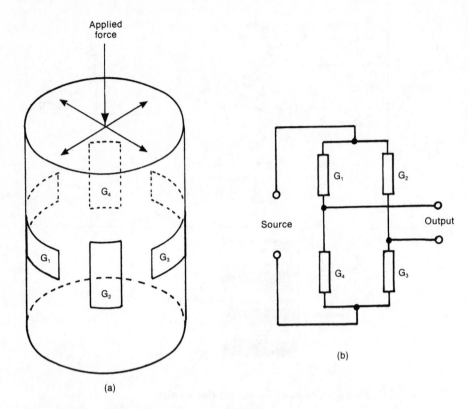

Figure 4.35 Load cell for measuring force

four identical gauges are employed in the bridge circuit, the system is automatically self-compensating for variations of ambient temperature.

For light loads, the elastic member will be constructed from a readily compressive material. For very high loads this is usually replaced with a stout steel cylinder.

Such a gauging system can be calibrated by progressive loading with standard masses (weights).

Acceleration and velocity

Since velocity is the rate of change of position and acceleration is the rate of change of velocity, these parameters can be derived from each other using differentiating or integrating circuits in association with amplifiers to provide the scaling factors. As force has been shown to be proportional to acceleration, in theory any transducer capable of measuring force can also be used to measure acceleration.

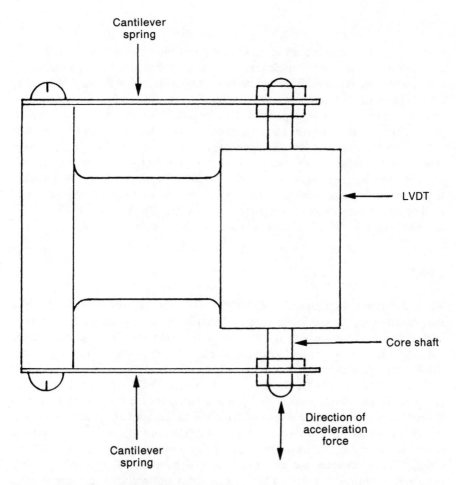

Figure 4.36   An acceleration transducer

One popular method is shown in Figure 4.36, where a LVDT is mounted on a substantial frame using a pair of cantilever springs. When subjected to either an accelerating or decelerating force along the axis shown, the central core deflects to generate an output signal proportional to the force and hence the acceleration. If this signal is integrated, the new output becomes proportional to the velocity. In a similar way, the output from a pulse counter/timer circuit designed to provide a velocity measurement will give the acceleration value after differentiation.

Either a tachogenerator or a shaft encoder can be used to provide the basis of angular velocity measurements. Differentiating such output signals then produces a value proportional to the angular acceleration.

Flow

Gas flow can be measured using a pair of thermistors wired into a bridge circuit. Both are held at the same ambient temperature (higher than the temperature of the gas) but one is placed in the gas flow while the other is shielded from it. The flow reduces the temperature of the exposed thermistor and so unbalances the bridge. A turbine rotor supported in a liquid flow will rotate at a speed depending on the flow-rate. The movement of the blades may then be detected with either a capacitive or electromagnetic pick-up to provide the electrical signal. To measure the flow-rates of 'slurry' type liquids an electromagnetic method may be used that relies on the conductivity of the slurry. A magnetic field is created at right-angles to the direction of flow and e.m.f. will be generated on a pair of probes that are placed mutually at right angles to both the flow and the magnetic field. (This is really the electrical generator principle.)

Level

There are many techniques available for the measurement of level. Each is designed to meet the special needs introduced by the wide variety of products to be handled and their effect on the system environment. The materials range from liquids to powders and granules, while the environments may vary from the benign to the explosive or corrosive.

Probably the simplest and best-known form of level measurement is that provided by the motor vehicle fuel-gauge system. Here a float is attached to a pivoted arm whose spindle is used to drive a slider across a linear potentiometer, in a circuit similar to that shown in Figure 4.22. The indicating device is simply a meter installed on the instrument panel and connected to read the output voltage. These devices are calibrated by progressively filling the tank with measured quantities of fuel. The system is not particularly accurate (except hopefully near to zero) mainly because of the non-uniform shape of the tank, but it is very simple and economical. Faults are usually those associated with open- or short-circuit wiring, worn potentiometer contacts or occasionally a punctured float. Bearing this in mind, it is fairly easy to track down a faulty component.

Figure 4.37 shows the principles of a number of techniques used for monitoring the tank or container levels in industrial applications. At least one of these would be suitable for use with any product, whether liquid, powder or granules, and in any environment.

Figure 4.37(a) shows a unique application of the opto-coupler technique, designed for use with liquids, to provide a very fast response time. The device is screwed into the tank, dome inwards, and when the fluid level is low there is a complete reflection of the light by the glass dome, between the LED and the

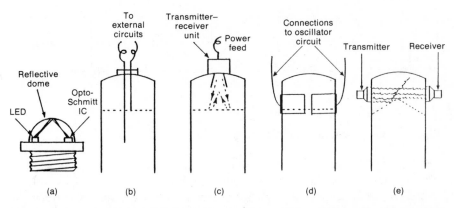

Figure 4.37 **Level detection: (a) opto-coupler; (b) for conductive liquids; (c) radar-type systems; (d) non-contacting capacitive system; (e) microwave system**

sensor IC. When the dome is covered, there is a rapid change in the refractive index at the reflecting layer and much of the light scatters into the liquid. The sensor has Schmitt-trigger characteristics, and responds rapidly to this sudden change of stimulus by changing the state of its output signal level.

Figure 4.37(b) indicates a technique that is suitable for detecting the level of a conductive liquid. One probe is immersed in the fluid and when the liquid level reaches the shorter probe it completes a circuit, thus providing a signal that can be used in any appropriate manner.

Figure 4.37(c) represents the principles of a number of different techniques, all relying upon the reflection of energy. Low-power radar transmissions can be used for monitoring the levels of liquids or powders in a continuous manner. The system is impervious to most process environments, including steam, dust, extreme temperature, high pressure and chemicals. The radar signal is transmitted in pulses through a window that is transparent to radio waves. The time taken for a reflection to be received back at the detector is representative of the level of the product in the tank. The detector system automatically uses this time duration to compute the level. Accuracies of better than ±5% can be obtained over depths as great as 20 m, and at high temperatures and pressures.

Ultrasonic sound waves can be used in a similar way and this technique is suitable for measuring the levels of either solids or liquids. These systems usually employ piezoelectric or ferroelectric devices to generate the wave energy. However, problems may arise due to false echoes created especially from granular products. Unless these effects are filtered out, they will give rise to a spurious response.

Infrared laser pulses are employed in a similar way and are used with solids or liquids that are not completely transparent. Again, this non-contacting system is impervious to most operating environments.

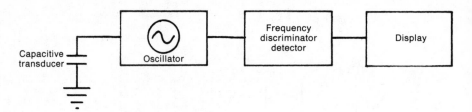

Figure 4.38   Level-detection circuit

Figure 4.37(d) shows one of the non-contacting level-monitoring systems that use a capacitive technique. The capacitor can be formed in several ways. If the container is non-metallic, then the plates can be formed around the periphery as shown. Alternatively insulated plates at the bottom and top of the tank can be employed. In both cases, the rising product level changes the dielectric constant ε_r as it replaces the air between the capacitor plates, to increase the capacitance value. Figure 4.38 shows how this capacitive transducer can be linked to an oscillator stage to control its frequency. As the level rises so does the capacitance value, causing the oscillator frequency to fall. This change of frequency can be detected by a frequency discriminator (a frequency-to-voltage converter) and the result displayed on an analogue meter. Alternatively a voltage-level detector circuit can be used to drive a bar graph or LED array display.

Figure 4.37(e) shows a technique using low-power microwave transmissions. The transmitter and receiver are mounted opposite each other on the tank which is equipped with radio-wave-transparent windows. As the product level in the tank rises, it interrupts the wave propagation and hence lowers the level of the received signal.

Temperature

Thermocouple devices are popular because of their fast response, approximately linear voltage/temperature characteristic, and ability to measure temperature over a small area. A range of instruments is available to cover temperatures from about $-200\,°C$ to $+1700\,°C$. Because the junctions represent a low impedance, the meters employed need to be fairly sensitive. The accuracy of these instruments depends upon the temperature of the cold junction (sometimes referred to as the *composite reference junction*). Although 'cold junction compensation' is usually incorporated in these instruments, they are commonly calibrated at an ambient temperature of 68 °F/20 °C or 32 °F/0 °C.

Resistance temperature detectors (RTD) use metallic conductors whose resistance increases proportionally with an increase in temperature (metals with a positive temperature coefficient). Recent developments employ a thin-film resistive pattern deposited on a chip of silicon. This is laser-trimmed to provide a precise resistance value, typically 2000 Ω at 20 °C. These devices have a fast linear response over a temperature range of about -40 °C to $+150$ °C. Since they are manufactured using IC technology, RTDs are compatible with the silicon ICs that are commonly used for signal conditioning.

Exercise 4.1

Using one of the proprietary training systems, measure and record the output of the d.c. tachogenerator for the full speed range, in both directions of rotation. Plot the calibration curve graphically and from this deduce the tachogenerator constant in terms of V/rev/min and rev/min/V.

Exercise 4.2

Using a linear potentiometer connected into a suitable circuit, measure and record the output voltages found at various displacements. Plot these results graphically to produce the voltage/displacement curve. Repeat this exercise with the pot loaded with resistors equal to (a) twice and (b) half its resistance. Plot the error curves for each on the previous diagram.

Exercise 4.3

From manufacturers' data sheets, select three different types of transducer or sensor. List and compare each of these in terms of linearity of transfer function, accuracy, resolution, range, sensitivity, bandwidth and response time. Hence match each transducer or sensor to a particular task.

Exercise 4.4

Use a CRO and two function generators to display a range of Lissajou's figures to confirm the results shown in Figure 3.4. Replace the CRO with an x–y plotter to obtain some hard copies of these diagrams. Note particularly the results obtained when using sine and square waves as the timebase.

Test questions

1 The following data were obtained from an experiment using a d.c. tacho-generator:

V_{out}(V)		3.2	7.0	13.8	20.8	28.3	35.2
Speed (rev/min)	100	200	400	600	800	1000

(a) Plot the graph and determine the tachogenerator constant in V/rev/min.
(b) What speed is represented by $V_{out} = 26.25$ V?
(c) What voltage would be produced at 500 rev/min?

2. The following data were obtained from experiments on a thermistor:

R (kΩ)	112	42	20	10	5	2	1	0.5
T (°C)	20	40	60	80	100	120	140	160

(a) Plot the characteristic and deduce whether this represents a device with a positive or negative temperature coefficient.
(b) Calculate the temperature coefficient for the range 20–40 °C.
(c) What temperature coincides with a resistance of 65 kΩ?

3 (a) State three pairs of dissimilar methods commonly used for thermo-couples.
(b) State two advantages and two disadvantages of thermocouples used for measuring temperatures.
(c) Consider the following statement: 'A thermocouple loop measures the hot junction temperature'. Is the statement true? If not, explain what it is that the thermocouple actually measures.

4 A particular linear potentiometer carries 200 turns with a total resistance of 1000 Ω. The maximum dissipation under working conditions must not exceed 100 mW.
(a) Calculate the maximum voltage that may be applied.
(b) Calculate the resistance resolution of the pot and its worst-case voltage resolution.

5 (a) State two applications of an opto-coupler.
(b) Explain how the circuit shown in Figure 4.39 operates with
  (i) a logic 1 at the input;
  (ii) a logic 0 at the input.

(c) State three reasons for using an opto-coupler in a circuit.

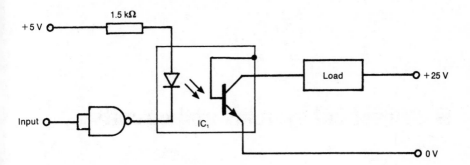

Figure 4.39 Circuit for test question 5

6 (a) Explain what is meant by the term *signal conditioning*.
   (b) Explain where a modulation scheme may be used to advantage in a control system.
   (c) Explain why a strain gauge is invariably used in conjunction with a second identical dummy gauge.
   (d) Define what is meant by the term *gauge factor*.

5 Practical systems and circuits

Summary

Observation of safe working practice. Identification and selection of modular control elements to form a simple system. Closed-loop temperature controller. Angular position controller. Analogue speed control system. Digital logic controlled burglar alarm. Set up and test a microprocessor controlled angular position controller. (Syllabus section 07, Practical assessments)

In addition, the Electronics Examination Board's practical test involves the following: measure voltages and record waveforms found at various test points within a system; diagnose faults to component level in a number of selected control systems.

Servicing control systems

When monitoring system behaviour, it is important to select test instruments that do not add extra loading to the system. Even unsuitable test leads can add unwanted capacitance that not only affects the instrument's frequency response, but can also have an adverse effect on system behaviour.

When testing and tuning system controllers, it is important that the effect of each adjustment is carefully studied. Never make two or more adjustments simultaneously because this leads to erratic and sometimes unstable control. It is also very often difficult to return the system to its original state if this rule is not followed.

110

It may seem strange in practical systems to find that even under stable conditions the comparator stage produces a non-zero output voltage. This will be due to the permanent losses in the final controlled element. For example, a motor even under no-load conditions generates bearing friction and requires energy to drive a tacho-generator, and an oven will always leak heat to its surrounding atmosphere. Each of these conditions requires that the driver stages must provide energy to counter the losses: hence the non-zero output from the comparator stage.

There is a need to recognize that in industrial applications the proportional controller is only generally used for systems with small loads, with moderately slow reaction times, and affected only by slowly varying disturbances. Further-more, provision needs to be made for the system to *fail safe*, particularly when driven up to the ends of the control range. For example, a position controller must be equipped with overriding limit switches to prevent mechanical damage.

Although the servicing of electronically controlled systems will in general follow conventional d.c. and low-frequency analogue procedures, it is important that fault-finding should be carried out in a very logical manner, with the measurements from each stage carefully considered before moving on to the next stage. It is important to develop this strategy because of the peculiarities of feedback systems.

It is useful here to restate the ways in which electrical components can fail. Resistors will very rarely develop low resistance values in use. They commonly go high-resistance (h/r) or develop an open circuit (o/c). Capacitors can become either open- or short-circuit (o/c or s/c). Inductors and transformers may become o/c or develop s/c turns that dissipate a significant amount of the circuit's energy. Excessive ambient temperatures or temperature cycling may cause the parameters of active devices such as diodes and transistors to change significantly. Ultimately this may lead to electrodes with o/c or s/c terminations. Fault-tracing in IC parts of the circuit is more problematical. Here it is import-ant to compare the pin voltages with those stated in the service data, paying particular attention to those pins that appear to be all at the same voltage, or unexpectedly at zero volts. Usually this signifies a short circuit which may either be internal to the IC, or associated with the external connections. The actual source of the problem can only be deduced by the removal of the IC.

Closed-loop temperature control system

The circuit of Figure 5.1 shows the general arrangement for this EEB training module. The heater element is represented by the resistor R_1, which is posit-ioned close to the temperature sensor IC_4. The temperature of the heater element is controlled by a pulse-frequency-modulated current and the sensor output is compared with a reference value. The difference signal is then used to control the system. The sensor, with a linear sensitivity of 10 mV/°C, provides an output that is proportional to the temperature generated by R_1. According to

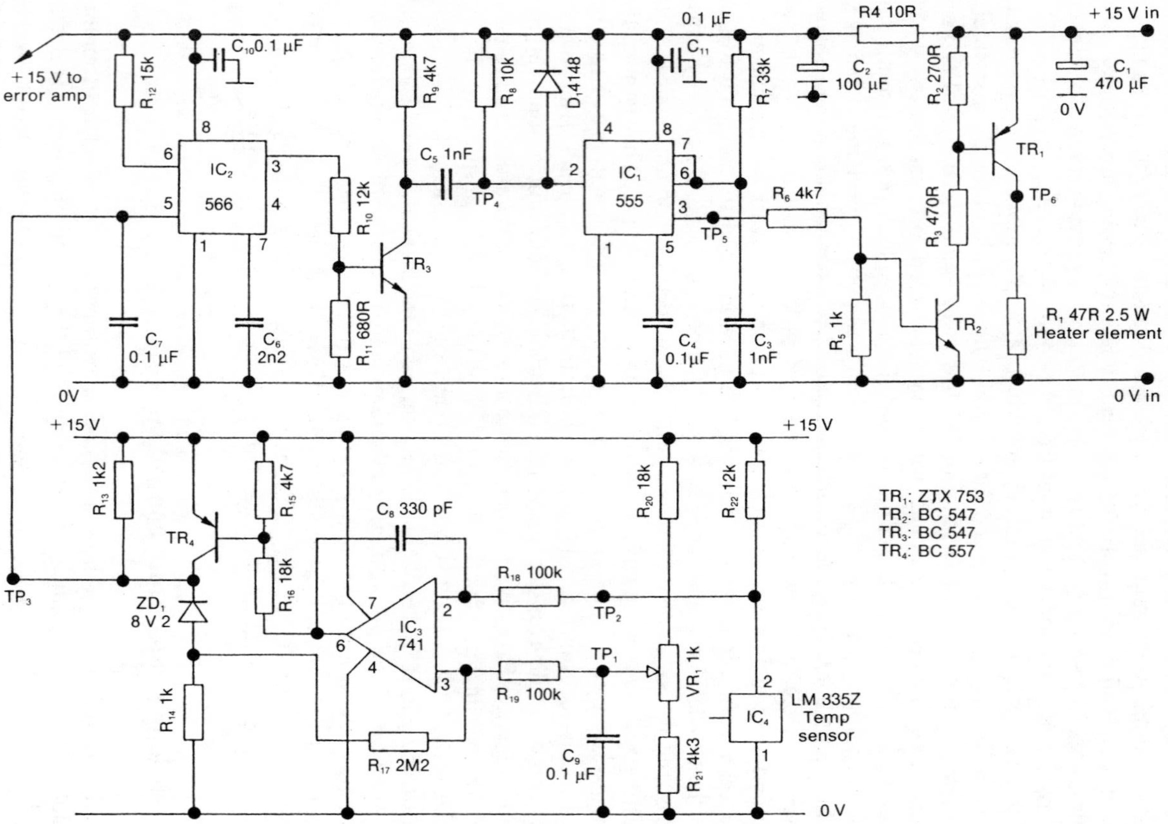

Figure 5.1   Closed-loop temperature-control system (courtesy of Electronics Examination Board)

112

the specification for IC_4, the actual temperature in degrees Celsius can be calculated from $(V_{out} \times 100) - 273.2$.

The sensor output voltage is compared with the reference value set by VR_1 in the 741 opamp IC_3 stage, which forms the comparator and error amplifier.

TR_4 and ZD_1 are used to level-shift the error signal output. The resistors R_{13} and R_{14} ensure that this control voltage is restricted to the range $+5$ V to $+15$ V, necessary to meet the drive conditions of IC_2.

The 566 device operates as a voltage-controlled oscillator (VCO) whose frequency is controlled by R_{12}, C_6 and the voltage applied to pin 5. With the components shown, this circuit can tune from about 10 Hz to over 20 kHz.

The circuit associated with TR_3 is used as an inverting stage to provide a negative-going trigger pulse to IC_1, a 555 timer stage operating as a monostable multivibrator. The output pulse width is controlled by R_7 and C_3 and with the component values shown, provides constant-width pulses of about 40 μs duration. The diode D_1 is used to suppress the positive-going transitions super-imposed on the trigger voltage.

The power amplifier stage is provided by the compound PNP/NPN transistor pair, TR_1 and TR_2. Since this stage operates from the common $+15$ V supply, it is necessary to arrange adequate decoupling between the pulse amplifier and the rest of the system. This is achieved by R_4, C_2 and C_1.

In operation, the voltage at TP2 is compared with that at TP1 so that IC_3 generates an error signal. After level-shifting, this appears at TP3 to provide the input to the VCO. Changes in this voltage cause the frequency of the 40 μs pulses delivered to the heater to vary. Thus an increase in frequency produces an increase in heating effect.

Test point signals:

TP1   A d.c. voltage in the range 2.75 V–3.40 V corresponds to a temperature range of 14–78 °C.

TP2   This shows a slowly oscillating d.c. voltage whose mean value depends upon the setting of VR_1.

TP3   A d.c. voltage in phase with that at TP2 and lying between $+5$ V and $+15$ V.

TP4   A frequency-variable pulse train depending upon the system drive requirements.

TP5 and 6 40 μs positive-going pulses with sharp transitions.

Angular position controller

The final drive element of this module, shown in Figure 5.2, consists of a d.c. motor coupled to a potentiometer via a 600:1 reduction gear box. The potenti-ometer VR_2 provides the feedback signal proportional to a position restricted to a maximum range of 270°. The circuit shows how this feedback signal is

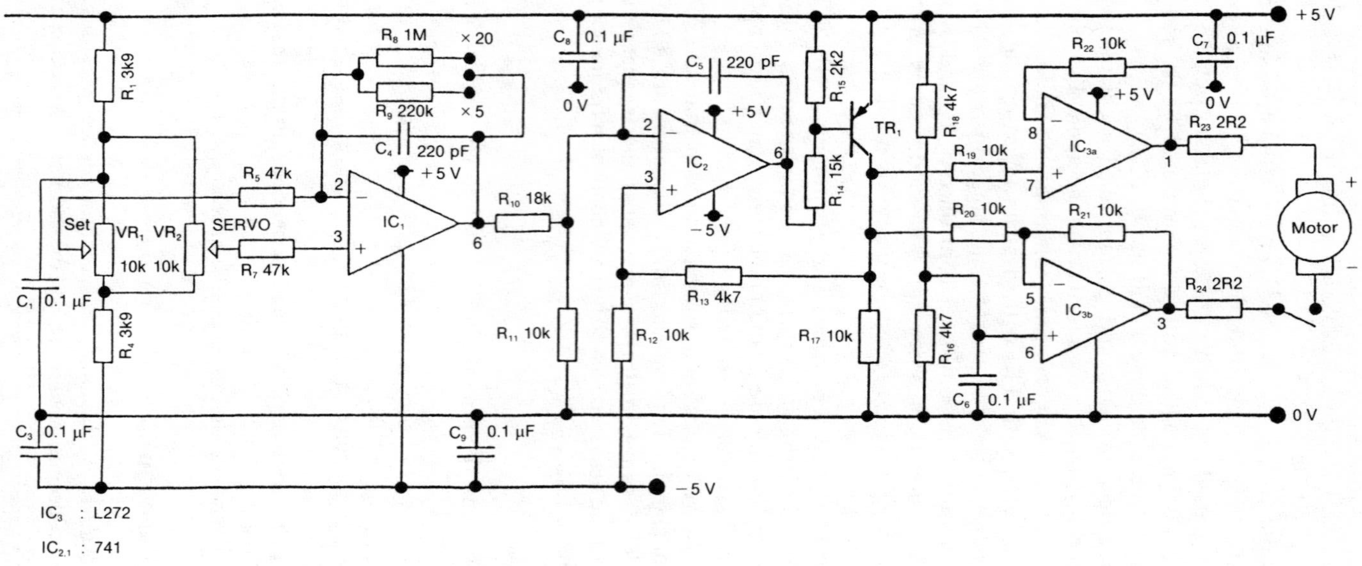

Figure 5.2 Angular position control system (courtesy of Electronics Examination Board)

Table 5.1   D.c. test voltages (Motor switched OFF, VR$_1$ and VR$_2$ sliders set to 0 V)

Pin No.	1	2	3	5	6	7
IC$_1$	—	0	0	—	0.3	—
IC$_2$	—	0.1	0.1	—	0.1	—
IC$_3$	2.5	—	2.6	2.5	—	2.5
TR$_1$ collector 1.5 V						

compared with a reference value set up on a similar-valued component by IC$_1$. This comparator and amplifier stage is equipped with switched gain control. The error signal is further amplified within a second opamp stage IC$_2$. The circuit associated with TR$_1$ converts the bipolar amplified error signal with a zero volts mean, into a monopolar signal centred on $+2.5$ V, as required for the drive to IC$_3$. This stage uses a dual power opamp to provide the necessary differential motor voltage derived from a single $+5$ V line.

The effects of mechanical drag on the system can easily be demonstrated by setting the amplifier gain to $\times 5$. It will also be found that the maximum range of the servo pot will be somewhat less than 270°. By comparison, the best system response is obtained with $\times 20$ gain setting. If both gain switches are set to off, the open-loop gain becomes very high and this leads to overshoot and instability.

Any faults that allow the system to behave in an open-loop manner but leave the motor powered can cause damage to the servo pot. An additional motor power switch has therefore been provided for testing under these conditions.

Voltage measurements should ideally be taken using a high-impedance meter. Note in particular that while the d.c. outputs at pin 6 of both 741 opamps swing about a mean of zero volts, the output at the collector of TR$_1$ swings about $+2.5$ V. D.c. test voltages are given in Table 5.1.

Analogue speed controllers

Figure 5.3 shows a circuit capable of controlling the speed of rotation of a small d.c. motor by making use of the back e.m.f. across the motor armature. When the armature of such a motor is not moving, normal current flowing through the armature produces only a small voltage drop, because of the low resistance of the armature. When the armature rotates, however, an e.m.f. is generated because the motor is now acting as a generator. The amplitude of this back e.m.f. is proportional to the speed of the motor.

In the circuit of Figure 5.3, the back e.m.f. is sensed and compared to the voltage at the slider of the potentiometer VR$_1$. The output of the opamp 741, which is used here as a comparator, controls current flow into the armature, so regulating motor speed to a value which gives a back e.m.f. equal to the voltage set by the potentiometer.

115

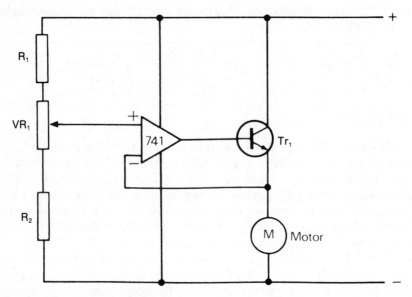

Figure 5.3   A speed controller for a small d.c. motor

In large motors, the use of a tachogenerator to control speed is more usual. It is indeed unavoidable when no back e.m.f. signal can be obtained (as is the case with many types of a.c. motor). The output generated by the tacho may be rectified, and compared with a d.c. voltage. The difference signal is then used to increase or decrease current flow through the motor until the error signal becomes zero.

A motor control system of the tachogenerator type may rely on either transistors or thyristors according to the motor power requirement. Either a.c. or d.c. motors can be controlled in this manner.

The block diagram of Figure 5.4 shows a possible future module development. This uses the same pulse-frequency-modulation technique that was applied to the temperature controller. The d.c. motor is directly coupled to an a.c. tachogenerator which produces an output whose frequency is proportional to the speed of rotation. This output is compared with the frequency generated by the reference oscillator which is under the control of the set speed potentiometer using a phase-locked loop (PLL). The error signal is therefore a d.c. voltage proportional to the phase difference. This is applied to the voltage-controlled oscillator (VCO) as a correcting influence. The pulse generator produces constant-width pulses, but at a frequency controlled by the VCO. The greater the pulse frequency, then the greater will be the average motor drive current and hence its speed.

A more elegant approach might replace the a.c. tacho with a shaft encoder which would produce a higher output frequency. This would allow the reference oscillator to be run at a correspondingly higher and more convenient frequency.

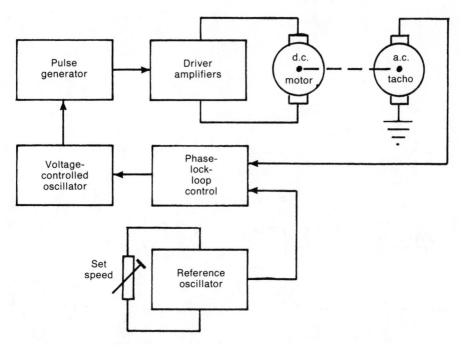

Figure 5.4   Speed-control system

Difficulties with such a circuit can occur at start-up. Provided that the two frequencies are within the loop bandwidth, the PLL will produce progressive lock-up as the frequencies converge. If the frequencies are outside the bandwidth, then a start-up circuit in parallel with the VCO will need to be employed.

Car burglar alarm system

See Figure 5.5. When power is applied with the *arm* switch open, T_1 is held on owing to the base current through R_5, D_2 and R_1. This provides a reset signal to the *alarm period* monostable IC_2 (555) and the *alarm triggered* latch IC_5.

Closing the *arm* switch triggers the *exit* delay monostable IC_1 (555). This holds T_1 on for a period set by R_3 and C_2 (about 10 s) after which T_1 is turned off, releasing the resets on IC_2 and IC_5.

If any *door switch* is now closed, this will set the *triggered latch* and T_2 will be turned off. This allows C_{12} to charge via R_{19}. After an *entry delay* period set by C_{12}, R_{19}, R_{20} and R_{21}, T_3 will be turned on, and T_4 will be turned off to trigger the alarm period monostable IC_2 via an inverter in IC_6.

The output from the *alarm period* monostable (time approximately 75 s, set by R_7, C_5) releases the reset on the *horn oscillator* astable IC_3, sounding the horn via a relay at a rate of about 1 Hz. (In this module, the horn is simulated by

117

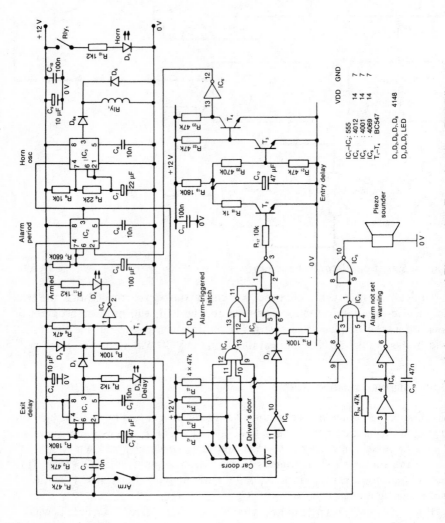

Figure 5.5   Car burglar alarm circuit (courtesy of Electronics Examination Board)

118

LED D_5.) This action also resets the *alarm triggered* latch via D_8 so that, when the *alarm period* has timed out, the alarm can be retriggered by any subsequent door switch closures.

At any time the *arm switch* may be opened to *reset and disarm* the entire circuit, with the exception of the *exit delay* monostable.

When the *arm switch* is in the open (disarmed) position, opening the driver's door will enable the *alarm not set* warning to sound via gates in IC_4 and IC_5. The tone is generated by the clock circuit associated with IC_6.

Microcomputer-controlled tasks

These tasks are written specifically for running on the EMMA microcontroller training unit shown in Figure 5.6. However, the programs will run on any of the earlier microcomputers that use the 6502 processor chip. The three tasks presented here are intended to aid the certification of each examination candidate's ability to set up and test a microcomputer-controlled system that performs a single task of angular position control.

The stepper motor used is a four-phase device with a basic step angle of 7.5°. By modifying the input step sequence, this can be changed to half steps of 3.75°. The input step sequences for these are shown in Table 5.2 and the codes produce anticlockwise rotation. (Reversing the code sequence causes the motor to run clockwise.) Note that the code sequences repeat cyclically and therefore all movements are incremental from the starting position.

In the normal 7.5° step mode, the number of steps per revolution is simply $360/7.5 = 48$ step/rev. The speed in rev/min is given by

$$\frac{\text{steps}}{\text{s}} \times \frac{60}{48} = 1.25 \times \frac{\text{steps}}{\text{s}}$$

In the half-step mode there are 96 steps per revolution, so that the speed in rev/min is given by

$$0.625 \times \frac{\text{steps}}{\text{s}}$$

If attempts are made to make the motor run too fast, its limited acceleration will cause steps to be missed and errors will arise.

For the EMMA, the stepper motor module is driven from the microcontroller's 5 V supply with its windings 1 to 4 consecutively connected to Port A PA_0 to PA_3 in sequence.

Task 1

To run the motor at 20 rev/min anticlockwise in full-step mode. To rotate at 20 rev/min, there must be $20/1.25 = 16$ step/s. Hence there will need to be a

Figure 5.6   EMMA microcontroller and stepper motor (courtesy of LJ Technical Systems Ltd)

Table 5.2

Step	I/P1	I/P2	I/P3	I/P4	Step angle	Hex code
1	0	0	1	1	7.5°	03
2	0	1	1	0	"	06
3	1	1	0	0	"	0C
4	1	0	0	1	"	09
5		Repeat sequence				
1	0	0	1	1	3.75°	03
2	0	0	1	0	"	02
3	0	1	1	0	"	06
4	0	1	0	0	"	04
5	1	1	0	0	"	0C
6	1	0	0	0	"	08
7	1	0	0	1	"	09
8	0	0	0	1	"	01
9		Repeat sequence				

delay of approximately $1/16$ s $= 62.5$ ms between pulses (this approximation is acceptable because pulse time is very small compared with the delay time).

The program therefore has three components, for which the flowcharts are shown in Figure 5.7:

1 initialization;
2 output pulses to motor;
3 delay between steps.

The program listing is shown in Table 5.3. The delay period is obtained by making 49 (31H) calls to the subroutine with a basic delay of about 1.29 ms.

Port A data direction register is at memory location 0901H, the data register is at 0903H and the lower four lines are set as outputs.

The drive sequence 03, 06, 0C, 09 is stored in locations 02B0 onwards.

Task 2

Adapt the system to stop after 20 complete revolutions.

This is achieved by modifying the program by adding a module that counts the steps and stops after 20 revolutions or 960 steps. The flowchart is shown in Figure 5.8 and the program listing in Table 5.4.

960 steps $= 03C0H$ and this requires two bytes which are loaded by the initialization subroutine into memory locations 0020 and 0021.

The count subroutine is loaded from address 02C0 onwards. Make the small changes to the main program and run and test the new task.

121

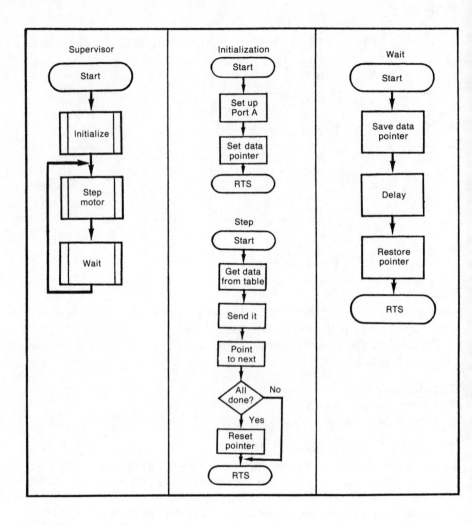

Figure 5.7   Flowcharts for task 1 (courtesy of LJ Technical Systems Ltd)

Task 3

Modify and test the programs:

(a)   for a count of 5 revolutions;
(b)   to run at 15 rev/min;
(c)   to run clockwise at 30 rev/min.

122

Table 5.3 Program listing for task 1 (courtesy LJ Technical Systems Ltd)

```
                        1          ;EXERCISE
                        2          ;**************************
                        3          ;
                        4          ;
                        5          ORG 0200H
                        6          ENT 0200H
                        7          ;
                        8          ;MAIN SUPERVISOR MODULE
                        9          ;**********************
                       10          ;
0200  20  40  02       11          JSR        INIT
0203  20  60  02       12 START:   JSR        STEP
0206  20  A0  02       13          JSR        DELAY
0209  4C  03  02       14          JMP        START
                       15          ;
                       16          ;
                       17          ;INITIALIZATION MODULE
                       18          ;*********************
                       19          ;
                       20          ORG 0240H
                       21          ;
0240  A9  03           22 INIT:    LDA#       03H
0242  8D  01  09       23          STA        0901H
0245  A9  0F           24          LDA#       0FH
0247  8D  03  09       25          STA        0903H
024A  A2  00           26          LDX#       00H
024C  60              27          RTS
                       28          ;
                       29          ;
                       30          ;STEP MODULE
                       31          ;***********
                       32          ;
                       33          ORG        0260H
                       34          ;
                       35          ;Fetch data pointed to by x
                       36          ;and output, then handle x
0260  BD  B0  02       37 STEP:    LDA        DATA,X
0263  8D  01  09       38          STA        0901H
0266  E8              39          INX
0267  E0  04           40          CPX#       04H
0269  D0  02           41          BNE        DONE     (026D)
026B  A2  00           42          LDX#       00H
026D  60              43 DONE:     RTS
                       44          ;
                       45          ;
                       46          ;DELAY MODULE
                       47          ;************
                       48          ;
                       49          ORG 02A0H
                       50          ;
02A0  8A              51 DELAY:    TXA
02A1  A0  31           52          LDY#       31H
02A3  A2  FF           53 WAIT2:   LDX#       FFH
02A5  CA              54 WAIT1:    DEX
02A6  D0  FD           55          BNE        WAIT1    (02A5)
02A8  88              56          DEY
02A9  D0  F8           57          BNE        WAIT2    (02A3)
02AB  AA              58          TAX
02AC  60              59          RTS
                       60          ;
                       61          ;
                       62          ;DATA TABLE OF DRIVE CODES
                       63          ;**********************
                       64          ;
                       65          ORG 02B0H
                       66          ;
02B0 03 06 0C 09
                       67 DATA:     DAB        03H 06H 0CH 09H
                       68          ;
```

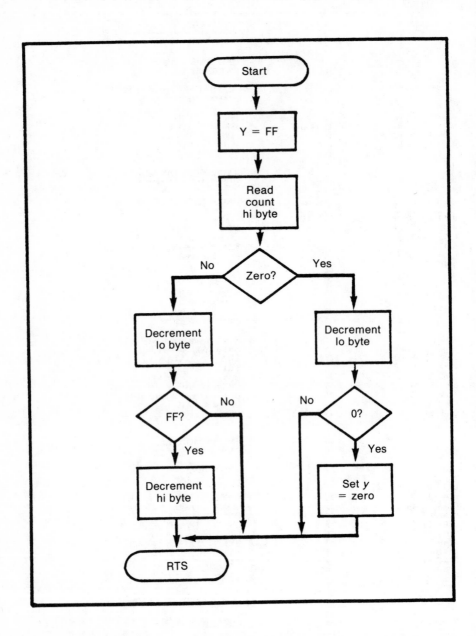

Figure 5.8 Flowchart for task 2 (courtesy of LJ Technical Systems Ltd)

Table 5.4   Program listing for task 2 (courtesy LJ Technical Systems Ltd)

```
                        8              ;MAIN SUPERVISOR MODULE
                        9              ;**********************
                       10              ;
                       11              ;Modified to call count
                       12              ;routine and test result
0200  20 40 02         13              JSR      INIT
0203  20 60 02         14 START:       JSR      STEP
0206  20 A0 02         15              JSR      DELAY
0209  20 C0 02         16              JSR      COUNT
020C  C0 FF            17              CPY #    FFH
020E  F0 F3            18              BEQ      START     (0203)
                       19              ;Stop in current position
0210  4C 10 02         20 STOP:        JMP      STOP
                       21              ;

                       22              ;
                       23              ;INITIALIZATION MODULE
                       24              ;**********************
                       25              ;
                       26              ORG      0240H
                       27              ;
                       28              ;Modified to set step count
0240  A9 03            29 INIT:        LDA #    03H
0242  8D 01 09         30              STA      0901H
0245  A9 0F            31              LDA #    0FH
0247  8D 03 09         32              STA      0903H
024A  A2 00            33              LDX #    00H
024C  A9 03            34              LDA #    03H
024E  85 21            35              STA      21H
0250  A9 C0            36              LDA #    C0H
0252  85 20            37              STA      20H
0254  60               38              RTS
                       39              ;

                       80              ;
                       81              ;16 BIT STEP COUNT MODULE
                       82              ;**********************
                       83              ;
                       84              ORG      02C0H
                       85              ;
                       86              ;Routine follows flow
                       87              ;chart     0200
                       88              ;is low byte, 0021 high byte
                       89              ;
02C0  A0 FF            90 COUNT:       LDY #    FFH
02C2  A5 21            91              LDA      21H
02C4  F0 0D            92              BEQ      YES       (02D3)
02C6  A9 FF            93              LDA #    FFH
02C8  C6 20            94              DEC      20H
02CA  C5 20            95              CMP      20H
02CC  D0 0B            96              BNE      FINI      (02D9)
02CE  C6 21            97              DEC      21H
02D0  4C D902          98              JMP      FINI
02D3  C6 20            99 YES:         DEC      20H
02D5  D0 02           100              BNE      FINI      (02D9)
02D7  A0 00           101              LDY #    OOH
02D9  60              102 FINI:        RTS
```

(a) For 5 rev/min there need to be 240 = 00F0H steps. The initialization subroutine is therefore changed to

```
024C  A9  00   LDA# 00H
024E  85  21   STA    21H
0250  A9  FO   LDA# F0H
0252  85  20   STA    20H
```

(b) For running at 15 rev/min, 15/1.25 = 12 steps/s are needed, with a delay of approximately 83 ms. Therefore with a basic subroutine delay of approximately 1.3 ms, there need to be 83/1.3 = 64 = 40H calls to the delay routine. The data in memory is thus changed as follows:

```
02A1  A0
02A2  40  LDY# 40H
```

(c) To run at 30 rev/min clockwise: 30 rev/min = 24 steps/s and this requires a step time of about 42 ms.
   Number of calls to basic delay = 42/1.3 = 32 = 20H. Thus change memory locations as follows:

```
02A1  A0
02A2  20  LDY# 20H and then reverse the data in the table to give
02B0  09  0C  06  03
```

Exercises

The exercises associated with Chapter 5 should concentrate on taking measurements, recording waveforms and interpreting the results, together with fault-finding to component level on the modules described.

Test questions

1 Refer to Figure 5.1. Describe the effects caused by the following component failures:
   (a) R_3 o/c;
   (b) R_7 o/c;
   (c) R_{11} o/c;
   (d) C_3 o/c;
   (e) ZD_1 o/c;
   (f) ZD_1 s/c.

2   Refer to Figure 5.2. Describe the effects caused by the following component failures:
    (a) R_1 o/c;
    (b) R_5 o/c;
    (c) R_{10} o/c;
    (d) R_{16} o/c;
    (e) R_{19} o/c;
    (f) R_{23} o/c.

3   Refer to Figure 5.5. Describe the effects caused by the following component failures:
    (a) R_1 o/c;
    (b) R_3 o/c;
    (c) R_{20} o/c;
    (d) R_{24} o/c;
    (e) C_5 o/c;
    (f) D_{6a} o/c.

Appendix 1   Answers to test questions

Chapter 1 Basic control systems

1 (a)   As the set-input level voltage is reduced, the error signal becomes negative and reduces the drive current to the heater via the power amplifier. The oven now cools through natural heat losses until the feedback voltage is practically equal to that represented by the new set-temperature level.

   (b)   The sensor output will fall to zero under this fault condition. The error signal therefore becomes positive and this drives the heater current up to maximum.

2 (a)   The ROM holds the necessary operating codes for the microcomputer to function in a wide range of different applications. The RAM holds the user instruction codes and data so that the microcomputer can function within a given specific application.

   (b)   To change the user-demanded operating temperatures, it is necessary for the operator to access the specific memory location that holds this data item. As soon as the binary code for 90° has been entered, the oven will start to cool because the error signal is now negative and this, via the power amplifier, reduces the oven heater current. As the temperature falls, the error signal falls towards zero. Eventually the system will stabilize at the new temperature setting.

3 (a)   (i)   If at a time t the setting of R_1 is suddenly moved to $+10$ V, the

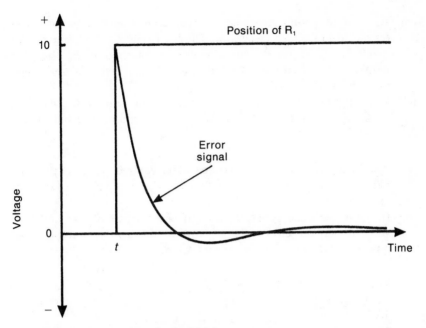

Figure A1.1   Answer to question 3(a)

non-inverting input to the comparator is presented with a step signal as shown in Figure A1.1. The error signal thus becomes high and positive so that the power amplifier provides a high drive current to the motor. After the initial inertia, the motor will run near maximum speed in the forward direction. At first, the feedback signal will be small but increasing. The error signal during the same period will be falling, so that the motor speed progressively reduces until it stops at the new controlled position with the error signal near to zero.

(ii)   The power amplifier input is in fact the error signal and has a waveform as indicated in Figure A1.1.

(b)   Assuming that R_2 is a linear potentiometer, 0 V will exist at the midpoint. After the fault condition occurs, this point would be at -5 V. If R_1 was set to a negative value, the system would drive R_2 to take up a corresponding negative voltage level, but with a positional error. If R_1 was set in the positive part of the range, the system would try to stabilize at the most positive voltage level available (0 V). The system would therefore be driven up to the potentiometer end-stop with the possibility of mechanical damage as well as a positional error.

limit the current flowing in the potentiometer and restrict the control range available.

(b) As the loading on the motor falls its speed will tend to rise, as will the output from the tachogenerator. The error signal will become negative and this will reduce the drive current to the motor via the power amplifier. The motor speed will thus quickly stabilize to its set speed to meet the new demands of the load.

(c) When the feedback loop becomes open-circuit automatic control will cease. The motor speed will rise to a maximum with only limited manual control via VR_1.

5 (a) Amplification in the feedback loop will be required whenever the sensor provides only a low level of output or whenever an impedance mismatch occurs.

(b) In many cases the system final controller consists of a motor-driven valve or similar device. These require considerable electrical drive power and so amplifiers are again necessary.

6 (a) Mechanical backlash will produce positional errors that will fluctuate between positive and negative depending upon the direction of drive.

(b) This condition is equivalent to electrical backlash. It will add to the system offset which may or may not be centred about the desired mean position.

Chapter 2 Rotating machines, relays, solenoids and actuators

1 (a) By separately reversing the polarity of the voltage applied to the field winding FF' and the armature AA'.

(b) By using a variable resistor to vary either the field or armature currents.

(c) Since both armature and field windings are in series, any change of current in one is accompanied by an equal change in the other. An increase in motor loading would cause the motor speed to fall, drawing a greater armature current. The corresponding increase in field current would cause the motor speed to fall further. This action, akin to positive feedback, thus produces a motor with a poor torque/speed characteristic.

2 (a) As P_1 is pressed relay RL_1 is energized, contacts A_1 and A_2 close, the motor starts to run and contacts A_1 will cause the relay to remain energized after P_1 is released.

(b) When P_2 is pressed its contacts short-circuit the relay coil and RL_1 releases. The motor then stops as contacts A_2 open.

(c) R_1 acts both as a voltage dropper, allowing a lower voltage relay to be operated from the same supply as the motor, and as a current limiter for the various contacts. D_1 acts as a shunt to remove any back e.m.f. generated as the motor switches on and off.

(d)   The power failure lasts for a period longer than the normal relay release time so that RL_1 releases and the motor stops. Since the relay has released, the hold contacts A_1 are now open and the motor cannot restart until P_1 is again pressed.

3   (a)   50 Hz is equivalent to 3000 rev/min. For three pole pairs the rotor turns for ⅓ revolution for each energization. The motor's synchronous speed is therefore $3000/3 = 1000$ rev/min.

(b)   Stepping angle $= 360°/(8 \times 3) = 15°$.

(c)   Number of pulses required $= 840°/15° = 56$.

4   A servo motor needs to have a low inertia so that it can respond rapidly to commands. It also needs to have a high starting torque in order to overcome stiction. The motor therefore has a smaller diameter rotor for low inertia and a longer rotor to provide the necessary torque. Furthermore, the field and armature windings are energized separately. Generally the armature is powered from a constant d.c. source, while the field is fed from a controlled source via an amplified error signal.

5   (a)   Over the normal operating range, the torque/speed characteristic is practically linear, with torque falling as the speed rises. The torque is thus inversely proportional to the motor speed.

(b)   Again, the speed/voltage characteristic is practically linear but with the speed being directly proportional to the voltage.

6   Solenoids, relays and contactors all rely upon the electromagnetic effect of a current flowing through a coil attracting a ferromagnetic armature or core. The term 'solenoid' is usually applied to a device that is used for converting electrical energy into some form of mechanical motion or control. Relays and contactors are both electromagnetically controlled switches. The term 'relay' is applied to relatively low-power switching devices, while 'contactor' describes a device used for high-power switching applications.

An actuator is any device that converts energy from a control system into mechanical movement.

Chapter 3 Measurements and instrumentation

1   The y channel amplifier must now be calibrated; see Exercise 3.2.

Using a 1 kHz sine wave input to the y channel, set the generator output level and CRO attenuator to produce a trace of 5 cm peak-to-peak. Gradually increase the generator frequency, noting the value at which the trace amplitude falls to $5 \times 0.707 = 3.535$ cm peak-to-peak (about 3.5 cm). This is the upper cut-off frequency, and since the y amplifier must have a d.c. response, it is also the amplifier bandwidth.

2   For Figure 3.9(a):
   (a)   Waveform A, peak to peak $= 4$ cm $\times$ 4 V/cm $= 16$ V.
       Waveform B, peak to peak $= 2$ cm $\times$ 4 V/cm $= 8$ V.
   (b)   Waveform A leads B by 3 cm which represents 3 cm $\times$ 100 ms/cm $=$ 300 ms.
   (c)   Periodic time $= 5$ cm $\times$ 100 ms/cm $= 500$ ms
       Frequency $= 1/500$ ms $= 2$ Hz.
   For Figure 3.9(b):
   (a)   Peak-to-peak amplitude $= 2.4$ cm or 2.4 cm $\times$ 100 mV/cm $= 240$ mV. Peak amplitude is therefore $= 120$ mV.
   (b)   A leads B by 1.5 cm and this represents 1.5 $\times$ 100 μs/cm $= 150$ μs.
   (c)   1 wavelength $= 4$ cm and A leads B by 1.5 cm, therefore this represents $360/4 \times 1.5 = 135°$.
   (d)   Periodic time $= 4$ cm $\times$ 100μs/cm $= 400$ μs. Therefore frequency is the reciprocal of this $= 2.5$ kHz.

3   A CRO would be used to detect which, if any, of the stepping pulses were absent. If a pulse is absent at any one input, this may be the result of a short circuit at this pole coil or the failure of the drive circuit. If the pole coil were open-circuit, the motor would still be inoperative and the drive pulse would not have been absent.

   The resistance of the suspect coil can readily be compared with that of the operating poles using a multirange ohmmeter.

   If the stepping pulse was absent at the driver stage, the CRO could again be used to follow the pulse voltage through a discrete component circuit, with a multimeter being used to detect the faulty component. Had the driver stage been an IC, then the final fault conclusion would depend upon the state of its d.c. supplies and the control input signals, all of which could be measured with a multirange meter.

4   With the I and Q signals input to the external x and y inputs a circle should be produced if the 90° of phase difference is present. One of the two channels (I or Q) would then be adjusted to achieve this. In practice, because the sensitivities of the x and y deflection systems are different, a circle is not always produced. In this case, it would be sufficient to obtain an ellipse whose major axis was vertical. In the general case, the phase angle between the two inputs can be evaluated as indicated in Figure A3.1. With the ellipse

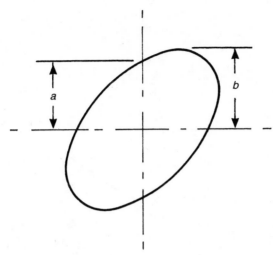

Figure A3.1   Answer to question 4

centred on the x and y graticules, the ratio of the height a to the peak height b is the sine of the phase angle, i.e. $a/b = \sin \theta$, where θ is the phase angle which can be evaluated using the arcsine function on a calculator.

5 (a) To record the drift in system parameters for quality control purposes. Depending upon rate of changes, the UV or chart recorder would be suitable.

   (b) To be able to record transient effects which could be evaluated later and at leisure. Suitable application for a single-channel CRO and camera.

   (c) To provide test parameters when commissioning a new system. This type of data might usefully be stored on a magnetic tape cassette.

6 Variation of motor speed would produce a variation in the data rate on replay. The system clock would then have difficulty in locking to this signal and so the data would be corrupted.

Chapter 4 Transducers and sensors

1 (a) From the graph, shown in Figure A4.1, the tachogenerator constant can be found from;
       $35 \text{ V}/1000 \text{ rev/min} = 0.035 \text{ V/rev/min}$

   (b) For 26.25 V output the speed would be 750 rev/min.

   (c) At 500 rev/min the output would be 17.5 V.

2 (a) The graph of this characteristic is shown in Figure A4.2; the negative slope indicates that the device has a negative temperature coefficient.

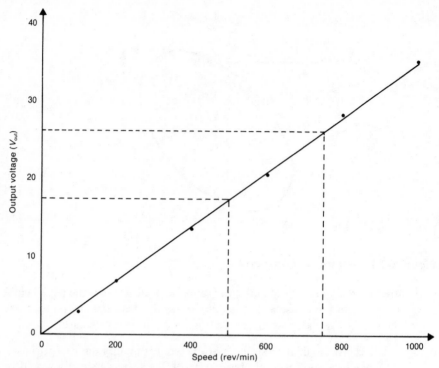

Figure A4.1   Answer to question 1

(b) The region between 20 and 40 °C is almost a straight line. Therefore the coefficient over this limited range can be found from

$$-70/20 = -3.5 \text{ k}\Omega/°C$$

(c) At a resistance of 65 kΩ, a temperature of 33 °C is indicated.

3 (a) The metals are chosen to maximize the contact potential for a particular temperature range. The pairs include: iron and copper–nickel alloys (iron–constantan) (0.05 mV/°C); copper and copper–nickel alloy (copper–constantan) (0.03 mV/°C); nickel–chromium alloy and copper–nickel alloy (nichrome–constantan); nickel–chromium alloy and nickel–aluminium–manganese alloy; platinum and platinum–rhodium alloy. Generally, copper–constantan types are used at lower temperatures, while platinum–rhodium types are preferred for the higher ranges.

(b) Advantages:

  (i)   Over a restricted temperature range they have a reasonably linear response.

134

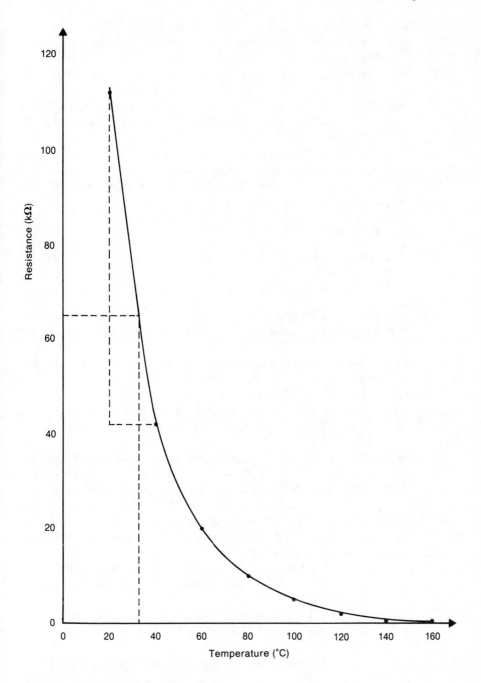

Figure A4.2   Answer to question 2

(ii)　Being very small, they can be inserted into small spaces.

(iii)　They have a rapid response to a change of temperature.

Disadvantages:

(i)　Several devices are necessary to cover a wide range of temperatures.

(ii)　Because of the small output and very low impedance, they need to be coupled to sensitive meters or used in conjunction with amplifiers.

(iii)　Because of the application, any associated amplifer must have very stable temperature characteristics.

(c)　The statement is false. The device responds to the difference between the temperatures of the hot and cold junctions.

4　(a)　The maximum voltage can be calculated as follows;

$$V^2/1000 = 100\,\text{mW}$$
$$V^2 = 100 \times 10^{-3} \times 1000$$
$$V = \sqrt{100} = 10\,\text{V}$$

(b)　Resolution $= 1000\,\Omega/200$ turns $= 5\,\Omega/\text{turn}$.

Worst-case voltage resolution $= 10/200 = 50\,\text{mV/turn}$.

5　(a)　(i)　Pulse-counting device used to measure the rotation of a slotted disc.

(ii)　In a shaft-encoder device.

(iii)　As a switching element in petrol engine ignition systems.

(iv)　As an interface between any two circuits where electrical isolation is critical.

(b)　With reference to Figure 4.39, the NAND gate acts as an inverter. A 1 input provides a 0 at the cathode of the LED which is now forward-biased. The diode emits light, activates the detector and causes the current to flow through the load. A logic 0 input provides a 1 at the LED cathode so that both ends of the diode are now at $+5$ V. The diode is now non-conducting and, as a result, the load is de-energized.

(c)　Reasons for using opto-couplers.

(i)　There is a very high degree of isolation between input and output.

(ii)　Because a light beam has no electrical impedance, there is no signal matching problem.

(iii)　They have a wide bandwidth and fast switching response.

(iv)　The coupling path is unaffected by electromagnetic interference.

(v)　An opto-coupler is very much smaller than the alternative relay.

6　(a)　Signal conditioning is required wherever the output from a transducer or sensor is too small, or not of the correct form to drive a system controller or display device. The signal conditioner is therefore essentially an amplifier. This may include frequency-compensation components (filtering) or impedance-matching devices.

(b) Where the feedback path from transducer to comparator is very long, the coupling path may well introduce severe attenuation or electromagnetic interference. In such cases, the use of a modulated carrier, which requires the use of an additional modulator and demodulator, can resolve the problems.

(b) When two similar gauges are connected in series in a bridge circuit, both will generate the same degree of temperature variation. The bridge configuration makes this effect self-cancelling. The only unbalance effect is then produced by the one gauge that is exposed to the strain being monitored.

(d) This effectively describes the sensitivity of the gauge. It is the ratio of the fractional change of resistance to the fractional change of strain.

Chapter 5 Practical systems and circuits

1 (a) With R_3 o/c both TR_1 and TR_2 are cut off, there will be no pulsing at TP_6 and the heater element temperature will be low. The pulse frequency at TP_5 will increase owing to the loss of loading on IC_1.

(b) With R_7 o/c, the voltages at TP_5 and TP_6 will be permanently high. TR_1 is saturated and maximum current flows through the heater element. In practice, this will dissipate more than the rated 2.5 W.

(c) When R_{11} is o/c, the voltage at TP_4 will be high and the 555 timer will not change state. The voltages at TP_5 and TP_6 will both be low, as will be the temperature of R_1.

(d) When C_3 is o/c, IC_1 is timed by R_7 and just the circuit stray capacitance. The pulse width will thus be very much reduced.

(e) If ZD_1 is o/c the voltage at TP_3 will be high and IC_2 will produce no output.

(f) If ZD_1 is s/c the voltage at TP_3 will be low and IC_2 will again produce no output.

2 (a) With R_1 o/c the set and servo sliders will both be at -5 V and the system will be dead. Similarly, if R_4 is o/c, the sliders will be at $+5$ V and again the system will be dead.

(b) With R_5 o/c there is no inverting input to IC_1 and so the set position control will be inoperative.

(c) If R_{10} is o/c, there will be no motor movement and most of the system voltages will be normal.

 (d) When R_{16} is o/c the motor will only run in the anticlockwise direction. Similarly, when R_{19} is o/c, the motor will only run in the clockwise direction.

 (e) With R_{23} o/c there will be no motor drive current. All other voltages will be normal.

3 (a) With R_1 o/c the alarm is permanently armed. There will be no reset when the arm switch is opened.

 (b) An o/c R_3 produces a permanent exit delay when the arm switch is closed. A similar effect will be produced by C_2 s/c.

 (c) When R_{20} is o/c the alarm period monostable IC_2 will never be triggered because T_3 is held off through lack of bias.

 (d) If R_{24} is o/c the clock is inoperative and so there will be no 'alarm not set' warning: similarly if C13 is s/c.

 (e) With C_5 o/c the alarm period will be very short.

 (f) With D_{6a} o/c the system will operate normally up to IC_3 but there will be no drive to operate the horn relay.

Appendix 2   Examination structure

The following examination structure is provided for the award of the Joint Part 2 Certificate in Electronics Servicing of the City and Guilds and the Electronics Examination Boards.

Core studies to be taken by all candidates:
224–2–11   Analogue Electronics Technology (MC)
224–2–12   Analogue Electronics practical assignments (in course)
224–2–13   Digital Electronics Technology (MC)
224–2–14   Digital Electronics practical assignments (in course)

Options. Candidates may enter either one or both of:
224–2–15   Television and Radio Reception Technology (written)
224–2–16   Control System Technology (written)

Practical examination. Candidates may enter one or both, appropriate to the above options:
224–2–17   EEB Practical test in Television and Radio Technology
224–2–18   EEB Practical test in Control System Technology

The assessments need not all be entered in the same year. The candidate can build up a series of credits towards the ultimate award of the certificate over a period of time.

Appendix 3 Abridged Part 2 Syllabus (index version)

Note: For complete information, the reader is referred to the City and Guilds Part 2 Syllabus.

The student is expected to be able to demonstrate competence in setting up, testing and fault-finding in basic control systems. He/she must also demonstrate a general command of basic electrical and electronic principles.

07, Control Systems option

7.1 Describe the operation of basic industrial control systems. Explain the terminology associated with the system elements. Explain the purpose of system devices associated with microprocessor-controlled systems. Describe the operation of continuous closed-loop systems for the control of temperature, position and speed. (Chapter 1)

7.2 State the basic principles of rotating electrical machines, relays, solenoids and actuators. Compare the relative merits and the applications of pneumatic, hydraulic and electrical actuators. (Chapter 2)

7.3 Describe the principles and applications of a range of test and measuring instruments. Select appropriate instruments for particular tasks and state the limitations of these instruments. Determine the constants or transfer functions for tachometers and potentiometers. (Chapter 3)

7.4 Describe the principles, characteristics and applications of various types of transducer. Describe the operation of circuits incorporating these devices.

Describe an appropriate transducer for a specific task of measurement or control. (Chapter 4)

08, Science background

003   Measuring instruments. Selection of a suitable instrument for both analogue and digital applications. The interpretation of results. The characteristics and limitations of various instruments. Instrument accuracy and calibration.

004   Transducers. State the purpose of these devices in electronic circuits. Describe the construction and characteristics of a range of devices.

006   Integrated circuits, transformers and displays. Compare the relative merits of silicon and germanium devices. Recognize device characteristics. Describe ways of testing various semiconductor devices. State the basic construction of both thick- and thin-film ICs. Describe the transformer principle and its various applications in electronic circuits. Perform calculations of voltage, current, impedance and turns ratio for an ideal (lossless) transformer. Compare the construction of transformers designed for specific applications. Explain how electrostatic and electromagnetic shielding is provided. Describe the operation and principles of LED and LCD (liquid crystal displays) and the relative advantages of each. Explain the construction of multisegment displays and the need for decoders and drivers.

Appendix 4   EEB practical tests

The test is presented in two sections. The candidate is expected to demonstrate his/her competence to perform a series of analogue and digital measurements using multimeters, double-beam oscilloscopes, logic probes and signal sources. In the second part each candidate is expected to be able to find faults in both analogue and digital circuits to component level.

Measurement tests

The candidate is allowed 30 minutes in which to carry out both static and dynamic measurements on a working circuit, using multimeters and oscilloscope. He/she has also to demonstrate the ability to sketch the time-related waveforms found at various test points in the circuit.

Fault-finding

The candidate is allowed 1 hour 30 minutes in which to locate three faults in different basic systems to component level and present a comprehensive report on the tests applied, the results found and the conclusions. The faulty systems used will be appropriate to the option of Control Systems and will include a temperature-control system, a car alarm and an angular position control servo system.

Appendix 5　Assessment checklist (Control Systems: Section 07)

In a practical situation, each candidate is expected to observe safe working practices.

Identify and select modular control system subsections to form a simple closed-loop system for temperature control.

Set up and test a microcomputer-controlled system to perform a single task for angular position control.

Measure and record voltages and waveforms at the following test points in a continuous speed-control system: error detection system; signal-processing stage; power amplifier output stage; final control elements; input and output transducers.

Diagnose a single fault to component level in each of the following closed-loop systems: temperature; speed and angular position control; car alarm.

Appendix 6 Surface-mount component codes

Many of these devices are too small to add the usual identification codes and, for this reason, surface-mount (SM) components should be retained in their packages until required. Devices that are marked usually use a two- or three-character coding as tabulated below:

A = 1	M = 3	Y = 8.2	0 = $\times 10^0$
B = 1.1	N = 3.3	Z = 9.1	1 = $\times 10^1$
C = 1.2	P = 3.6	a = 2.5	2 = $\times 10^2$
D = 1.3	Q = 3.9	b = 3.5	3 = $\times 10^3$
E = 1.5	R = 4.3	d = 4	4 = $\times 10^4$
F = 1.6	S = 4.7	e = 4.5	5 = $\times 10^5$
G = 1.8	T = 5.1	f = 5	6 = $\times 10^6$
H = 2	U = 5.6	m = 6	7 = $\times 10^7$
J = 2.2	V = 6.2	n = 7	8 = $\times 10^8$
K = 2.4	W = 6.8	t = 8	9 = $\times 10^{-1}$
L = 2.7	X = 7.5	y = 9	

For three-character applications, the first two digits yield the base number and the third the multiplier. For example, 472 = 4.7 kΩ or 4700 pF; 4R7 = 4.7 Ω.

The two-character version consists of a character and a multiplier. For example, A1 = 10 Ω or 10 pF; N3 = 3.3 kΩ or 3300 pF.

Appendix 7   Report writing

Readers following the BTEC Level N unit of Control Systems are expected to write formal reports of their findings from various assignments. These brief notes are provided as a guide to making this task easier and to giving the final report greater impact.

When writing a report, remember that some of the readers may not have the technical expertise of the writer. Therefore you should write in a readable, logical and interesting manner. Explain and present any technical terms or expressions so that they can be easily understood.

Avoid the use of jargon, shorthand and abbreviations if possible. If you have to use them, then define each term at its first appearance in the report. If used carefully and sparsely, jargon, particularly those terms that have an amusing connotation, can help to make a report more readable for the less technical individual.

If necessary, obtain professional assistance and make use of reference libraries, but remember to identify all sources of help.

Produce the report in a series of logical sections, starting with an introductory section that describes the aims and objectives of the exercise.

If necessary obtain help to organize the layout of the document. Care with this feature can often improve the impact of the report.

Use only standard symbols and diagrams and adhere to standard in-house practice. Ensure that all drawings and listings are suitably annotated so that they can be easily referred to while reading.

Any conclusion that you draw should be fully justified. If at all possible, avoid taking a biased viewpoint. If there are alternative views, present each one fairly and try to make a carefully reasoned selection.

It is important that you develop an objective style of writing that is not too personal.

Avoid using long sentences if possible. However, varying the length of sentences can be effective provided that the text flows in an informative and interesting manner.

Avoid using long words. They can give the reader the impression that the writer is trying to show a degree of superiority.

Don't use a long rambling approach. Try to drive up to a point in a short and logical manner.

A good report takes time to write. Draw up a skeleton outline and flesh this out slowly in a logical way. A good report should flow in the manner of a computer program. A well-written report should provide a high degree of satisfaction to the author and gain the grateful thanks of the reader.

Although the overall presentation is important to produce a good first impression, it is useful to remember that in an engineering world the contents are normally more important than the wrapping.

Appendix 8
POLYGLOT GLOSSARY

English	Danish	Dutch	French
Accumulator	Akkumulator	Accumulator	Accumulateur
Address	Adressere	Adres	Adresse
Amplifier	Forstærker	Versterker	Amplificateur
Antenna	Antenne	Antenne	Antenne
Battery	Batteri	Batterij (or Accu)	Batterie
Cable	Kabel	Kabel	Câble

Capacitors

English	Danish	Dutch	French
Capacitor, fixed, ceramic dielectric	Kondensator, fast, keramisk dielektrisk	Condensator, vaste, mica	Condensateur, fixe, diélectrique en céramique
Capacitor, fixed, electrolytic, aluminium	Kondensator, fast, elektrolytisk, aluminium	Condensator, vaste, aluminium	Condensateur, fixe, électrolytique, aluminium
Capacitor, fixed, electrolytic, tantalum	Kondensator, fast, elektrolytisk, tantal	Condensator, vaste, tantaal	Condensateur, fixe, électrolytique, tantale
Capacitor, fixed, mica dielectric	Kondensator, fast, glimmer dielektrisk	Condensator, vaste, mica	Condensateur, fixe, diélectrique en mica
Capacitor, fixed, paper dielectric	Kondensator, fast, papir dielektrisk	Condensator, vaste, papier	Condensateur, fixe, diélectrique en papier
Capacitor, fixed, plastic dielectric	Kondensator, fast, plastisk, dielektrisk	Condensator, vaste, kunststof	Condensateur, fixe, diélectrique en plastique

German	Italian	Swedish
Akkumulator	Accumulatore	Ackumulator
Adresse	Indirizzo	Adress
Verstärker	Amplificatore	Förstärkare
Antenne	Antenna	Antenn
Batterie	Batteria	Batteri
Kabel	Cavo	Kabel
Festkondensator, Keramik-Dielektrikum	Condensatore, fisso, dielettrico in ceramica	Kondensator, fast, keramisk dielektrisk
Festkondensator, elektrolytisch, Aluminium	Condensatore, fisso, elettrolitico alluminio	Kondensator, fast, elektrolytisk, aluminium
Festkondensator, elektrolytisch, Tantal	Condensatore, fisso, elettrolitico, tantalio	Kondensator, fast, elektrolytisk tantal
Festkondensator, Mika-Dielektrikum	Condensatore, fisso, dielettrico a mica	Kondensator, fast, glimmer dielektrisk
Festkondensator, Papier-Dielektrikum	Condensatore, fisso, dielettrico in carta	Kondensator, fast, papper dielektrisk
Festkondensator, Plastik-Dielektrikum	Condensatore, fisso, dielettrico in plastica	Kondensator, fast, plast dielektrisk

149

English	Danish	Dutch	French
Capacitor, variable air dielectric, differential	Kondensator, variabel, luft dielektrisk differential	Condensator, variabele, lucht diëlectricum, differentiële	Condensateur, variable, diélectrique air, différential
Capacitor, variable air dielectric, trimming	Kondensator, variabel, luft dielektrisk, trimming	Trimmer-condensator, variabele, lucht diëlectricum	Condensateur, variable, diélectrique air, trimmer
Capacitor, variable air dielectric, tuning	Kondensator, variabel, luft dielektrisk, indstilling	Afstem-condensator, variabele, lucht diëlectricum	Condensateur, variable, diélectrique air, d'accord
Capacitor, variable ceramic dielectric, trimming	Kondensator, variabel, keramisk, dielektrisk, trimming	Trimmer-condensator, variabele, keramisch diëlectricum	Condensateur, variable, diélectrique en céramique, trimmer
Capacitor, variable mica dielectric, trimming	Kondensator, variabel, glimmer dielektrisk, trimming	Trimmer-condensator, variabele, mica diëlectricum	Condensateur, variable, diélectrique en mica, trimmer
Capacitor, variable, plastic dielectric, trimming	Kondensator, variabel, plastisk dielektrisk, trimming	Trimmer-condensator, variabele, kunststof diëlectricum	Condensateur, variable, diélectrique en plastique, trimmer
Capacitor, variable, solid dielectric, tuning	Kondensator, variabel, massiv dielektrisk, indstilling	Afstem-condensator, variabele, vastestof	Condensateur, variable, diélectrique solide, d'accord
Channel	Kanal	Kanaal	Canal
Clip	Klemme	Klem	Attache

German	Italian	Swedish
Drehkondensator, Luft-Dielektrikum, Differential	Condensatore, variabile, dielettrico aria, differenziale	Kondensator, variabel, luft dielektrisk, differential
Drehkondensator, Luft-Dielektrikum, zum Trimmen	Condensatore, variabile, dielettrico aria, compensazione	Kondensator, variabel, luft dielektrisk, trimning
Drehkondensator, Luft-Dielektrikum, zum Abstimmen	Condensatore, variabile, dielettrico, aria, sintonia	Kondensator, variabel, luft, dielektrisk, inställning
Drehkondensator, Keramik-Dielektrikum, zum Trimmen	Condensatore, variabile, dielettrico in ceramica, compensazione	Kondensator, variabel, keramisk dielektrisk, trimning
Drehkondensator, Mika-Dielektrikum, zum Trimmen	Condensatore, variabile, dielettrico mica, compensazione	Kondensator, variabel, glimmer dielektrisk, trimning
Drehkondensator, Plastik-Dielektrikum, zum Trimmen	Condensatore, variabile, dielettrico in plastica, compensazione	Kondensator, variabel, plast dielektrisk, trimning
Drehkondensator, festes Dielektrikum, zum Abstimmen	Condensatore, variabile, dielettrico solido, sintonia	Kondensator, variabel, solid dielektrisk, inställning
Kanal	Canale	Kanal
Klemme	Fermaglio	Klämma

English	Danish	Dutch	French
Coaxial	Koaksialt	Coaxiale	Coaxial
Coil	Spole	Spoel	Bobine
Connecting strip	Forbindelses-strimmel	Verbindings strip	Lamelle de connexion
Crystal unit	Krystal-aggregat	Kristaleenheid	Ensemble à cristal
Dial	Nummerskive	Afleesschaal wijzerplaat kiesschijf	Cadran
Disc	Skive	Schijf	Disque
Earphones	Hovedtelefon	Hoofdtelefoon	Écouteurs
Field effect transistor	Felt effekt transistor	Veldeffekt transistor	Transistor à effet de champ
Frequency	Frekvens	Frequent	Fréquence
Fuse	Sikring	Zekering	Fusible
Fuse holder	Sikersholder	Zekering houder	Porte-fusible
Group board	Grupperings-tavle	Verdeelbord	Tableau de distribution
Hermetic seal	Hermetisk forsegling	Afdichting	Joint hermétique
Input	Indgangseffekt	Invoer	Entrée
Insulator, stand-off	Isolator, afstand	Isolator, afstand	Colonne isolante
Jack plug and socket	Jack-stikkontakt	Telefoonklink met plug	Fiche et douille de jack

German	Italian	Swedish
Koaxial	Coassiale	Koaxial
Spule	Bobina	Spole
Klemmleiste	Fascetta di collegamento	Förbindningsbleck
Kristalleinheit	Gruppo cristallo	Kristallenhet
Zifferblatt	Quadrante	Nummerskiva
Scheibe	Disco	Skiva
Kopfhörer	Cuffia radio-telefonica	Hörlurar
Feldeffekt-Transistor (Fieldistor)	Transistore a effetto di campo	Fälteffekt Transistor
Frequenz	Frequenza	Frekvens
Sicherung	Fusibile	Propp
Sicherungshalter	Portafusible	Propphållare
Anordnungstafel	Quadro del gruppo	Grupperingsbräda
Hermetische Abdichtung	Guarnizione ermetica	Hermetisk försegling
Eingabe	Entrata	Ineffekt
Isolator, Distanz	Isolatore, portante	Isolator, standoff
Klinkenstöpsel und Steckdose	Spina singola e presa	Jackpropp och uttag

English	Danish	Dutch	French
Knob	Knap	Knop	Bouton
Lamp	Lampe	Lamp	Lampe
Lamp holder	Lampeholder	Lamphouder	Douille de lampe
Level	Niveau	Nivo	Niveau
Loudspeaker	Højttaler	Luidspreker	Haut-parleur
Meter	Måler	Meter	Enregistreur
Microphone	Mikrofon	Microfoon	Microphone
Motor	Motor	Motor	Moteur
Output	Udganseffekt	Uitgangs-vermogen	Sortie
Plug and socket	Stikkontakt	Steker en stekerbus	Prises mâle et femelle
Printed circuit	Trykt Kredsløb	Gedrukte stroomkring	Circuit imprimé
Printed wiring connector	Trykt Ledningsfor-bindelse	Printplaat connector	Connecteur de câblage imprimé
Push-button switch	Trykkontakt	Drukknop schakelaar	Commutateur à bouton-poussoir
Radio frequency	Radiofrekvens	Hogefrequentie	Haute fréquence
Rectifier, metal	Ensretter, metal	Metaal gelijkrichter	Redresseur sec

German	Italian	Swedish
Knopf	Pomella	Knapp
Leuchtkörper	Lampada	Lampa
Leuchtkörperfassung	Portalampada	Lamphållare
Pegel	Livella	Nivå
Lautsprecher	Altoparlante	Högtalare
Zähler	Strumento di misurazione	Mätare
Mikrofon	Microfono	Mikrofon
Motor	Motore elettrico	Motor
Ausgabe	Uscita	Uteffekt
Stecker und Steckdose	Spina e presa	Stickontakt och utlag
Gedruckte Schaltungen	Circuito stampato	Tryckt kretslopp
Gedruckte Leitungs-verbindungen	Serrafili circuito stampato	Tryckt kabelförbindning
Druckschalter	Interruttore a puesante	Tryckknappsströms-tällare
Radiofrequenz	Radiofrequenza	Radiofrekvens
Gleichrichter, Metall	Raddrizzatore, metallo	Likriktare, metall

English	Danish	Dutch	French
Rectifier, semiconductor	Ensretter halvleder	Halfgeleider gelijkrichter	Redresseur semiconducteur
Rectifier, silicon	Ensretter silicum	Silicium gelijkrichter	Redresseur au silicium
Relay	Relæ	Relais	Relais

Resistors

English	Danish	Dutch	French
Resistor, fixed, carbon composition	Modstand, fast, Kulstofkom-position	Weerstand, vaste, koolmassa	Résistance, fixe, agglomérée de carbone
Resistor, fixed, cracked carbon	Modstand, fast, krak-kulstof	Weerstand, vaste, opgedampte kool	Résistance, fixe, carbone de craquage
Resistor, fixed, metal film	Modstand, fast, metalhinde	Weerstand, vaste, metaalfilm	Résistance, fixe, couche métallique
Resistor, fixed, oxide film	Modstand, fast, oksydhinde	Weerstand, vaste, oxidefilm	Résistance, fixe, couche d'oxyde
Resistor, fixed, wirewound, general purpose	Modstand, fast, trådomviklet, almindeligt formål	Weerstand, vaste, universele, draad	Résistance, fixe, bobinée, universalle
Resistor, fixed, wirewound, precision	Modstand, fast, trådomviklet, præcisions	Weerstand, vaste, precisiedraad	Résistance, fixe, bobinée, de précision
Resistor, variable, carbon	Modstand, variabel, kulstof	Weerstand, variabele, kool	Résistance, variable, carbone

German	Italian	Swedish
Gleichrichter, Halbleiter	Raddrizzatore, semiconduttore	Likritare, halvledare
Gleichrichter, Silikon	Raddrizzatore, silicio	Likritare, kisel
Relais	Relè	Relä
Festwiderstand, Kohlenstoff-zusammensetzung	Resistenza, fissa, composizione di carbone	Motstånd, fast, kolsammansättning
Festwiderstand, gesprungene Kohle	Resistenza, fissa, frammenti di carbone	Motstånd, fast, fragmenterat kol
Festwiderstand Metallfilm	Resistenza, fissa, pellicola	Motstånd, fast, metallhinna
Festwiderstand, Oxidfilm	Resistenza, fissa, pellicola, ossidata	Motstånd, fast, oxidhinna
Festwiderstand, drahtgewickelt, für Allegemeinzwecke	Resistenza, fissa, avvolgimento in filo, impiego generale	Motstånd, fast, trådlindad, allmänna ändamål
Festwiderstand, drahtgewickelt, Präzision	Resistenza, fissa, avvolgimento in filo, di precisione	Motstånd, fast, trådlindad, precision
Drehwiderstand, Kohle	Resistenza, variabile, carbone	Motstånd, variabel, kol

English	Danish	Dutch	French
Resistor, variable, wirewound, general purpose	Modstand, variabel, trådomviklet, almindeligt formål	Weerstand, variabele, universele draad	Résistance, variable, bobinée, universelle
Resistor, variable, wirewound, precision	Modstand, variabel, trådomviklet, præcisions	Weerstand, variabele, precisiedraad	Résistance, variable, bobinée, de précision

Switches

Key switch	Nøgle-afbryder	Druktoets-schakelaar	Manipulateur
Microswitch	Mikroafbryder	Microschakelaar	Micro-contact
Rotary switch	Roterende afbryder	Draai schakelaar	Commutateur rotatif
Slide-action switch	Glide-afbryder	Schuif-schakelaar	Commutateur à curseur
Toggle switch	Leddet afbryder	Tuimel-schakelaar	Tumbler
Sleeving	Overtræk	Mantel	Manchonnage
Terminal	Tilslutnings-klemme	Aansluitpunt	Borne
Transistor	Transistor	Transistor	Transistor
Transformer audio	Transformator audio	Trandformator audio	Transformateur, audio fréquence
Transformer IF	Transformator mellemfrekvens	Transformator midden frequent	Transformateur, fréquence intermédiaire

158

German	Italian	Swedish
Drehwiderstand, drahtgewickelt, für Allegemeinzwecke	Resistenza, variabile, avvolgimento in filo, impiego generale	Motstånd, variabel, trådlindad, allmänna ändamål
Drehwiderstand, drahtgewickelt, Prazision	Resistenza, variabile, avvolgimento in filo, di precisione	Motstånd, variabel, trådlindad, precision
Schlüsselschalter	Interruttore a chiave	Nyckelströmställare
Mikroschalter	Microinterruttore	Mikroströmställare
Drehschalter	Interuttore a rotazione	Roterande strömställare
Schiebeschalter	Interrutore scorrevole	Glid-strömställare
Kippschalter	Interruttore a levetta	Ledad strömställare
Umhüllungen	Manicotto	Hyslor
Anschluss	Terminale	Kabelfäste
Transistor	Transistore	Transistor
Transformator niederfrequenz	Trasformatore, audio	Transformator, lågfrekvens
Transformator, Zwischenfrequenz	Trasformatore, frequenza intermedia	Transformator, mellanfrekvens

English	Danish	Dutch	French
Transformer mains	Transformator lysnet	Transformator voedings	Transformateur, d'alimentation
Toroidal coil	Toroid-spole	Toroidespoel	Bobine toroïdale
Valve	Rør	Buis	Tube
Valve holder	Rørholder	Buishouder	Support de tube
Valve screen	Rørskærm	Buisscherm	Ecran de tube
Valve, subminiature	Lille miniaturrør	Subminiatuur buis	Tube subminiature
Wire	Ledning	Draad	Fil
X Plates	X-Afdriftpladen	X-Abuigplaten	Plaques de déviation horizontale
Y Plates	Y-Afdriftpladen	Y-Afbuigplaten	Plaques de déviation verticale

German	Italian	Swedish
Transformatornetz (Netztrafo)	Trasformatore linea principale	Transformator, huvudledning
Toroidspule	Bobina toroidale	Toroidspole
Röhre	Valvola	Rör
Röhrenfassung	Portavalvola	Rörhallare
Röhrengitter	Schermo valvola	Rörfilter
Kleinströhre	Valvola extra piccola	Subminiatyrrör
Draht	Filo	Ledning
X-Ablenkplatten	Piatti di deviazione orizzontale	X-plattor
Y-Ablenkplatten	Piatti di deviazione verticale	Y-plattor

Index